■ ■

HENRY MILLER

Brooklyn Intellectual
Paris Bohemian
World Celebrity

Here—in one volume—are some of the best writings of one of the most outspoken authors of the twentieth century.

Life, literature, art, obscenity . . . no matter what the subject Henry Miller expresses himself with exhilarating candor and originality. An independent thinker who scorns the dogmatic and attacks the phony, he probes controversial ideas with energy and insight.

Made up of stories, sketches and autobiographical notes, this masterful collection of Miller's work reveals the many facets of his talent, the versatility of his style and the hard, sharp brilliance of his mind.

"At his best Miller writes on a level of true expressiveness generating a kind of all-out poetry, at once genial and savage. . . . A great talent."
—Philip Rahv

■■

The Intimate
HENRY MILLER

WITH AN INTRODUCTION BY
LAWRENCE CLARK POWELL

A SIGNET BOOK

Published by THE NEW AMERICAN LIBRARY

CONTENTS

INTRODUCTION

Sooner or later everything comes in and goes out of a university library: books on French roulette and the dynamics of turbulent flow, on vector-analysis and psychoanalysis, missals and missiles, on flood and drought, law and disorder, books for and against, of good and evil, all free to all, a storehouse as powerful as any uranium stockpile, each book awaiting the touch of hand, the sight of eye which will release its energy.

Into this magnetic field there came one day in the spring of 1941 a small, erect man in conventional garb, carrying a checked cloth cap, who came to my desk and said, "I am Henry Miller. My publisher said when I reached L.A. to go out to UCLA and see Larry Powell, a librarian who reads books."

"Guilty," I said. "And sometimes on company time."

"Do you have any books by Jacob Boehme?" was Miller's first question.

"We'll go into the stacks and see," I said.

So into the great central book-stack we went in search of the German shoemaker–mystic of the 1600's, whose books influenced English mystical thought from William Penn to William Yeats. Our quest led us to the second underground level where, like an ore deposit, we found solid shelves of books on Religion and Philosophy, and one book in particular with a title Yeats thought one of the loveliest ever conceived—Boehme's *Aurora, or the Morning Redness in the Sky*.

I have never seen a man change so fast as Miller did when I put that book in his hand. He settled down on his haunches on the floor and began to leaf through it, read phrases, and talk more to himself than to me. Up to then he had been rather insignificant as a person; now he began to fill out and expand, to communicate and radiate energy.

"Somewhere in the Southwest I found myself wanting to read Boehme," he said, "and of course there was no library en route that would even have heard of, much less have Boehme on its shelves. It is worse than being without water, not to have a book when you want it. When are you through work? Four-thirty? Good. Come back for me then and we'll go out for a cup of coffee."

So I left Henry Miller reading on the cold floor, and when I returned two and a half hours later, he was still there, like the Buddha, smiling and joyful. And in the nineteen years since then our friendship, cemented in mutual bookishness, has flourished like the coast live oak, green the year round.

We had met back in 1931 on the staircase in the Faculty of Letters of the University of Dijon, where I was a graduate student and he a teacher in the Lycée Carnot, suffering the exile from Paris so marvelously described in *Tropic of Cancer*. Two people who passed on the stairs, neither making an impression on the other. No true meeting, perhaps, because there were no books on the stairs.

During those years after his arrival in Los Angeles, Miller lived near us in Beverly Glen, a bohemian backwater in the Santa Monica hills a mile from the university. Commuting back and forth, I ran a bookmobile service for him, endlessly fascinated by the variety of his interests, dropping off a book about the headwaters of the Blue Nile, picking up one about the guild of medieval cathedral builders, today books on bristles and Balzac, tomorrow a biography of Colette or a book about Paris. Either we had them or we got them for him, which is what a librarian is supposed to do.

We rendered a bit more than bibliographical service for Miller. *The Colossus of Maroussi,* his exuberant book about Greece, had appeared in the beautiful Colt Press format, and he wanted it translated into Greek. There was a Greek girl working in the library. When she and Miller met, it was combustion rather than translation that occurred.

When Miller moved to the Big Sur, we continued to give him help by mail. He made the library the depository for his manuscripts, papers, correspondence, and ephemeral publications, and there was commenced what has grown into the Henry Miller Archive, a vast collection documenting his transformation from Brooklyn intellectual to Paris bohemian to world celebrity. Along with Mark Twain, Jack London, and Upton Sinclair, Henry Miller is one of the widest read of all American writers.

Books were ever and always the bond between us. One night when we were driving from his home on Partington Ridge to the nearest telephone some fourteen miles down coast at Lucia, I asked Miller if he would write a piece on the importance of books and libraries in his life which I might have privately printed as a Christmas keepsake. He examined the idea with a few questions, punctuated by that characteristic meditative sound he makes—a cross between a groan, a grunt, and a sigh—and said he would have a try at it.

I returned to Los Angeles, and then I witnessed by the way Miller works. An idea rises in him like the headwaters of a river, first the merest trickling flow, gradually increasing to brook to stream to river, and finally to confluence with the sea. A page or two arrived, a few more, a chapter, another, and then, page after page, chapter upon chapter, the torrential manuscript which was to become *The Books in My Life*.

I was appalled by the prospect of my private printing bill. Likewise Miller was troubled by the thought that I would print only a few copies of this work which, rightfully, should reach the the widest possible audience.

"Would you mind," he finally queried me, "if we made this manuscript available to my publisher as a regular trade edition?"

I got off my own hook by replying, "Good Lord, no!"

And so the book took shape and the mail sacks between UCLA and Big Sur bulged, as Miller asked for a thousand and one references and confirmations. I accepted the ultimate dedication of the book on behalf of the entire library staff, who toiled to keep the furnace stoked.

There is a dichotomy, but no contradiction, between Miller the writer and Miller the man, between the violence of his view of life as recreated in his prose and the gentle manner of his actual way of life. *Live like a lamb,* Flaubert said, *so that you can write like a lion.* This has been Henry Miller's way, at least in the years I have known him. If he had not been fated otherwise, Miller would have made a good reference librarian, with a passion for knowledge, a sense of order, and a desire to communicate.

"Artesian" is an adjective I have always applied to Henry Miller—free-flowing, abundant, without need of pumping. So many writers are stingy-dry, selfishly working their talent, giving out only when they are getting in. All the years I have known him, Miller has been generous to the point of prodigality, giving all to anyone in need, whether it was literary aid or the money in his pocket.

Passing by his place one day in the Glen, with our younger son Wilkie in the car with me, I stopped to see if Miller was in need of more books. It was at the time of his "Open Letter" in the *New Republic,* calling for donations of money, food and clothing, in return for which he would send the donor one of his original watercolor paintings. A variety of clothing arrived, including an incongruous tuxedo which Miller spread like a scarecrow on the picket fence.

We found him at his easel, and after an exchange of greetings he observed my son, age seven, eyeing several shiny pennies on the table.

"Like money?" Miller asked.

Bug-eyed Wilkie nodded.

"Take those pennies then."

Wilkie carefully gathered them.

"Want more?" Miller persisted.

The child nodded his head.

Whereupon Miller began to light up and come to life. He turned his pockets out.

"If you like money, you shall have money," he cried, throwing coins on the table.

"Take it all!" and he swept the money into the lad's eager hands.

It added up to seventy-six cents. Wilkie, starry-eyed, ran out doors. It was the most money he had ever had at one time.

"It's every cent I have in the world," Miller said to me. "A useless sum to me; a fortune to him."

After that Wilkie liked, understandably, to visit Miller. Cash windfalls never recurred, but there was always some kind of abundance lavished on him by Miller. Keys, watches, colored shoelaces, all given in the spirit of, "You like it? Well then, take it!"

Carried over into the field of correspondence, this prodigality has become a problem to Miller, as people write to him from all over the world, to ask help of various kinds. The problem is one of time. How apportion it between the needs of others and his need to write his own work? Too many people seek to go beyond a writer's work and fasten on the man himself and suck him dry. Nevertheless at sixty-seven Henry Miller is still flowing. I expect he always will be. He has always had a capacity for lasting friendships, and with a variety of people such as the late Emil Schnellock, Anaïs Nin, Alfred Perlès, Lawrence Durrell, and his longtime publisher, James Laughlin.

A meal at Henry Miller's is a never-to-be-forgotten event, something of a religious ceremony, the food by candlelight, with Henry's outflow starting slowly, waxing stronger as the intake of food and drink warms the blood. He is one of the world's great talkers, and the greatest performances come at mealtime when the Staff of Life, the Meat and Wine, the Fruit and Cheese, have made the old master glow and radiate heat. Suddenly a key word triggers him and he launches on a dithyrambic *tour de speech* more pyrotechnical than any Royal Fireworks.

Once in the Glen, at a dinner cooked to perfection by my wife, the trigger word was *Marseilles*. Miller took it the way a trout takes a fly, and away he went, first talking at table, then rising and pacing the room, glass in hand, recalling the glories of France—people, food and drink, the riversweet ambiance of Paris, talking several parts in turn, questions and answers, an antiphonal monologue, his own delight mounting as he saw the pleasure in the others' eyes, an essentially impersonal performance, spokesman for life itself, focused and finding expression in the Boy from Brooklyn, the most original American writer since Walt Whitman and whose fame will eventually permeate his native land.

If an astrologer had told Henry Miller thirty years ago in Paris that the crowning years of his life would be spent on an isolated stretch of the Central California coast, he would have changed astrologers. Nothing seemed less likely. And yet it came to pass that in 1945 Miller quit smog-blighted southern California for the clear air of the Sur Coast, settling eventually in a cottage on Partington Ridge, high above the wind-blown Pacific. Fifty miles north, on Carmel Bay, lives Robinson Jeffers, the greatest poet of his time. It seems to me no accident that these two writers should have been drawn to this wild and beautiful coast. I can very well understand the reason: it is a creative region, where strong forces are available to those with the necessary transformers.

There in the company of this vital man and his wife Eve, loving, beautiful, and wise, I have found surcease from too much city; eating by Millerlight, talking of life, love, and learning—and of books, of course, those honeycombs of all three.

One need not go to Big Sur to partake of Henry Miller. There are his books, overflowing with the man himself, and immortal as man is not. The *Tropics* are generally unavailable in the lands of his native language, but enough has been legally published, and now this third paperbound selection, to satisfy readers' desire for writing that is strong, bold, personal, refreshing, and nourishing. Henry Miller belongs to the Unbeat Generation. Old-fashioned now, perhaps, yet joined with such outspoken men of good will as Rabelais, hands across the centuries, timeless, lifegiving, and free.

LAWRENCE CLARK POWELL

Los Angeles
December, 1958

REUNION IN BARCELONA

May 1st, 1954

Dear Fred:

In a few days it will be a year since we had our reunion. If fifteen years ago, when we were saying good-by to one another in London, any one would have predicted that our next meeting would take place in Spain—in Barcelona, of all places!—I would have laughed him down. The logical meeting place should have been Ibiza, or Ischia, or even the Island of Rhodes. However, we finally did meet again, that is the important thing. And now I can make a clean breast of it and tell you that when we parted in London I had little hope of ever seeing you again.

Since my return from Greece in 1940 it has been one long, uninterrupted struggle to keep my head above water. Thousands of dollars have passed through my hands, but that means nothing here. To live as well as an ordinary plumber or bricklayer demands an income such as only a pulp writer could hope to earn. No matter how handsome the check I receive, it all goes out the next day. There is no getting ahead of the game. Everybody is in debt, mortgaged to the hilt, from the national government (which sets the example) on down to the common laborer.

But I don't mean to dwell on my poverty, which I know is just a myth to you or to any humble citizen of Europe. There is a more sinister kind of poverty, a veritable deprivation, which life in America entails. I was made aware of it the moment I set foot on French soil. I mean—the lack of communion with one's own kind.

13

The instant I espied Georges Belmont and Maurice Nadeau at the Gare d'Orsay, where they had been waiting seven hours for us to arrive, I knew I was once again with human beings who spoke my language. From then on, wherever we went in Europe, it was nothing but happy *rencontres*. Even the bores, and they were few and far between, proved stimulating. Every now and then, while roaming the streets or riding a bus, an oft-repeated phrase of yours—"Joey, you've *got* to come back, you belong over here!"—would come back to me. And with what force!

Despite all the efforts I made to re-establish myself in America, despite the fact that I finally made a home for myself here in Big Sur, the first and only home I have ever known in my native land, despite the fact that it is a virtual paradise, this place, it is nevertheless not what I knew as home when I was living abroad. In France, no matter where I found myself, I was at home. Here, the moment I pass the boundary line which demarcates Big Sur from the rest of America I am in an alien world. And I mean an *alien* world. I am certain, for example, that if tomorrow I were plunked down in Peiping, Bombay or Cairo, I would feel more at home, more at ease, than anywhere in the United States. Try as I may, I cannot explain it to myself. Not entirely. Nor do I expect you to be able to, you who have never been a home body either. The great difference between us, and it's entirely to your credit, is that you know how to make yourself at home no matter where God sets you down. You would feel at home in your home town, dear old Vienna. There you are! For me there is no Vienna. Even the 14th Ward (Brooklyn), about which I have waxed sentimental in the past, is but a myth.

I've just stepped out to the edge of the cliff to take a leak. What a day! What a view! If you were here, right beside me, you'd say I was crazy to write as I've just been writing. You'd say: "I'm going to stay here forever. This is Heaven!" And I'd agree with you. It *is* Heaven. At least, *comme décor*. But standing there alone, adding my tiny trickle to the vast, empty Pacific, so calm, so blue, so mirror-like, standing there looking down the Coast with its huge, rolling hills dropping into the sea—forty miles of it

I can see in either direction—standing there bedazzled, awed sometimes, and ever reverent, mind you, nevertheless I sometimes catch myself murmuring: "If only it were the Mediterranean!" *If only* . . . At times I curse myself for venting such thoughts. Imagine being in Paradise and saying to oneself: "If only there were a touch of Hell!" That's what it amounts to, Joey. I'm straddling the fence. I want to have my cake and eat it too.

But do I? I ask myself that over and over again. *Do I?* And then, to ease my conscience, I tell myself that I was only pretending, that in truth I *am* content. "You poor bugger, you're *happy*, only you don't know it!" I say to myself. And to prove it I will begin to whistle or do a jig, or I will call the dog and explain to him how lucky he is to be living in a paradise.

Yes, as far as it goes, I am happy and I am content. The trouble is it doesn't go far enough. I could use a bigger dose of happiness, a bigger dose of contentment. I don't want to be content on four cylinders; I want a complete eight-cylinder sparkle and joy. Of course I'll never have it, thinking this way.

Suddenly, in the midst of all this silly shit, I recall certain stretches in Paris when I had nothing, not even food in my belly—yet I was happy, divinely happy. What's more, I *knew* I was happy. No "if only" . . . I *had* it, I *was* it, I *knew* it. Explain that to me, if you can! As the Japanese poet once expressed it—"Was I a man who dreamed of being a butterfly, or was I a butterfly dreaming myself to be a man?"

Last night, reading Giono's *Voyage en Italie*, I was struck by his frequent allusions to the subject of happiness. I have only traveled with him through a few cities thus far but already, I observe, he is impressed with the way the Italians manifest their contentment with life. He even pauses to reflect that the Italian *knows* when he is happy, whereas the Northerner does not. Talking about the right way to fry fish, he drops this: *"Vous n'imaginez pas comme tout est fait pour le plaisir. Il ne faut rien dédaigner. Le bonheur est une recherche. Il faut y employer l'expérience et son imagination. Rien ne paie de façon plus certaine . . ."*

Happiness! What I never tire of telling my American friends is that in the Villa Seurat days, and even before when there was little to laugh about, we laughed every day, and we laughed long and hard. Every time I saw you coming I would begin to smile and chuckle. Maybe you had come to tell me of some misfortune—that you hadn't had dinner the night before, or that you hadn't had an answer to the *pneu* you had sent your latest inamorata, or that your job was in jeopardy, or that your mother had just died— but you were laughing before you could get the words out of your mouth. Was there anything in those days that could possibly make us sad? Nothing I can think of now, unless it were the threat of expulsion from France. Certain of our friends, I recall, pretended to be highly incensed that we could be so merry, laugh so heartily, when men like Hitler and Mussolini were causing the world such woe. To be sure, these birds were never very gay birds, no matter what the condition of the world. Hitler and Mussolini simply provided them with the desired ammunition.

Shortly after the war ended there came a day here in Big Sur which I can only describe as a red letter day. It was the day I received the record which you and Durrell made in London expressly to cheer me up, expressly to entice me to join you. What a message that was! How I laughed and wept! Never did I feel so good, and never did I feel so lonely. When you broke into French, into that lusty, vulgar jargon of the street, when you began reeling off the names of streets, boulevards, alleys, cafés, wines, cigarettes, Metro stops, films, old friends, even the one-legged whore in Montmartre, I was fit to burst a blood vessel. It was like champagne and caviar, and it was diabolical too. Never was Paris so near yet so far away. Suddenly I had an image of you as you used to look when, feigning to be desperately in love, feigning to be broken-hearted, you would suddenly break into a rigadoon in the middle of the street. I saw the way your jaw would drop and your under lip protrude as you cried out mockingly to any female who happened to be

passing—*"Je t'aime! Je t'aime!"* In a few moments, the
fever past, you'd exclaim: "Shit, let's sit down somewhere
and have a drink." And then maybe you really would get
sad, for a minute or two, usually only until the *garçon* appeared with the drinks. Your sadness, of course, only made
us gayer. Whereupon you would become slightly annoyed,
feigning astonishment or indignation because we were so
heartless, so indifferent to your woes. But as soon as you
had taken a gulp the twinkle reappeared in your eyes, and,
to make amends for your pretended melancholy, you would
suddenly begin to make sport of the one you loved, or you
would savagely desecrate your mother's name, or you
would begin to wonder aloud how long it had been since
the last good lay . . . maybe as long ago as yesterday,
what! With that the day would really begin for us. Another
fine à l'eau, another Amer Picon, another *demi,* and we
were off on the merry-go-round. Somehow, do you remember, we always managed to find the money we needed for
whatever devilment we were up to. Everything failing, there
was always David Edgar, the beloved Edgar, to fall back
on. It was never too difficult to find him. Usually he could
be found at the Café Zeyer, expounding the latest Rudolf
Steiner to a neophyte. If not there, he was sure to be at the
Dôme or the Select. The funny thing about Edgar—really
touching, now that I think of it—was that he never said
no to us. He had no illusions about our integrity, yet he
never turned us down. You know, such people are getting
rarer and rarer.

But to get back. . . . That record really undermined
me. From then on it was only a question of ways and
means. Once, you may recall, I was on the point of leaving
with my little girl. When that fell through I was at the point
of despair. And then a miracle occurred, nothing less. Out
of a clear sky came a handsome check in payment of a debt
I had long ago wiped off the slate. In jig time I was on the
plane headed for Paris, and with me was Eve who had appeared at the crucial moment, like an angel from above.

Why didn't we go to London first, since you were the
one I wanted most to see? Because it was mid-winter, and
the recollection of my last visit to London was a grim one.
I had forgotten that Paris too can be disagreeable in winter.

As a matter of fact, it turned out to be the coldest winter I have ever known in Paris. I thought I would never see the sun again. Anyway, after a brief exchange by carrier pigeon, it was agreed that we would meet in Barcelona—in the month of May.

I can't tell you how dismal and woe-begone Barcelona looked approaching it by car. It brightened up, to be sure, when we got near the center of town. It even began to look a bit Spanish. But it was not the city I had dreamed it would be. Except for the Rambla and the narrow, winding streets leading off it, Barcelona impressed me as a hodge-podge of Brooklyn and Brussels. And then that bloody American Express office where we were supposed to meet! In Spain it goes by a different name . . . and it's always difficult to locate.

By the time twenty-four hours had elapsed, and we had not yet found each other, I was in a veritable fever. (And why was I so certain that you would be staying at the Hotel Vienna?) Fortunately, as if by telepathy, we had the same hunch at the same time—to go back to the American Express and leave a message.

Anyway, there I am, handing my message to the clerk at the desk and accepting the one you had left the day before. I shove yours in my pocket, intending to read it leisurely, and start down the stairs, with Eve right behind me. Suddenly I see a bald head below me, a polished, sun-burned, egg-shaped head (like Shakespeare's, I think to myself), and there you are fumbling with something in your hands and chuckling and clucking like a hen that has just laid a golden egg. "Joey!" you cried, the sweat pouring down your face, your lips drooling, your hands still fumbling with whatever it was. Thus we stood for a moment, as if shell-shocked, you at the bottom of the stairway and I at the top. (I could hear Eve behind me gurgling with delight.) In that swift down-gazing moment I registered the undefinable changes time had wrought; the next instant they were completely erased and you were standing before me as I have always known you, not a whit older, not a whit sadder, neither lean nor fat, neither muscular nor flabby, but just yourself, and from one ear to the other there was spread that unforgettable grin which you will wear to your dying day.

Today what stands out most about our reunion in Barcelona is this laughter which we indulged in, this hearty, hysterical, stomachic laughter which began the moment we met and never ceased until we separated forty-eight hours later. Even in my sleep I continued to laugh. All through Spain I laughed, all of us laughed, whenever your name was mentioned. I laughed not as a man does who is happy to find an old friend, a *copain,* a fond scallywag, I laughed as a man would laugh who suddenly met a messenger of the gods bringing him on a platter the most vivid, detailed memories of all the golden days of his life. In your presence all that was vital and precious in the carefree past became alive again. When you smiled a certain way, a daffy, baffling smile, or drooped your head sidewise like a horse, or pouted like a child who has just been reproved, when you grew red as a beet in ecstasy and the veins stood out in knots at your temples, or you let your tongue fall out like a panting dog, any one of these inimitable mimicries was sufficient to precipitate a whole landslide of convulsive memories. Whatever the trick or dodge, and you had a thousand of them up your sleeve, it never existed as an isolated phenomenon. With it there always came the ambiance of the intimate few who were part of the show, always the aroma of food and drink, the room we were sitting in, the café, the cinéma, the street noises, the hour of the day, the state of our purse, the project for the morrow, the book we were writing, the certitude that we were truly enjoying ourselves, the knowledge that the best life had to offer was to live it as we were then living it. Certainly no two individuals then living in Paris could have enjoyed themselves more than we did. Everything was gravy to us, including the blows and the hardships. *Starvation?* Meaningless, if one survives. The worst was semi-starvation. *N'est-ce pas?* Those days when we were famished, when we were desperate—or thought we were!—often ended gloriously. "The worst squall never outlasts the morning," as Lao-tse says.

The more wisdom I acquire the more I recognize the truth that the irresponsible ones, as the "right-thinkers" call them, grow gayer and more reckless with age. The "gay, old dogs," whom the wise Orientals describe as the true Masters, are not scoundrels, scallywags, rogues and rapscallions, but downright sinners, criminals sometimes . . . at least, in the eyes of the ignorant. And the more I think about it the more I am convinced that, whether you know it or not, you belong to this order of emancipated beings. With what relish I recall the alacrity and disgust with which some of our acquaintances gave up trying to convert you to their way of thinking. In their eyes you were always "hopeless." Even when you tried to play the game, when you pretended (for their sake) to be "converted," they were supremely dissatisfied. It was as though they knew that in accepting you, in making you a member, so to speak, of their little group, they were putting a worm in a barrel of ripe apples. How painfully they struggled to attain the grain of wisdom, or the enlightenment, they were searching for! And you who sat still, who made no struggle, no fuss, no effort, who even enjoyed watching others flounder about in their own stew, that *you* might possibly have it, *that* they never dreamed of. To them you were just a snail wearily climbing the slope of Fujiyama. It was beyond them to comprehend that you were being absolutely true to yourself, that, forgive the comparison, having elected to be a snail, you were taking your way snail-wise toward the land of bliss. Your readiness and willingness to move with equal dispatch toward God or the Devil completely disoriented them.

Come to think of it, I was nearing forty when I finally broke with my old ways. With most men that is the age when they muscle into their snail-like shells. As for those who have "a purpose in life," by the time they reach middle age they have become rather grim customers. *Wolverines,* I call them. Truth to tell, I was dangerously near becoming one of these ugly specimens myself about the time you appeared on the scene. Whenever I mention the fact that you "saved my life" I always hasten to amend it by adding —"I don't mean that he saved me from starvation alone. It was much more than that!" And then I blush to think how often I have employed this stock phrase—"So-and-so saved my life." How many, many times must I have been in danger of being snuffed out! And in what varied guises the Saviour always appeared to me! Really, sometimes it seems to me that my only contribution to life has been the opportunity I gave others to help themselves—by saving my life. I can carry it to such an extreme, this thought, that, when I think about it intently, it becomes absolutely clear to me that even those who were bent on injuring, humiliating or degrading me were really serving as my benefactors. In short, when I take the long view I see nothing but "salvation." And that's why it's so good to be a sinner, or just a renegade: letting others help you, letting them lift you up, you're giving them a rare chance to redeem themselves. Our worst enemies, if we have any, are the ones who refuse to let you be the snail you are, or the weasel, or the fox, or the maggot, or the glow-worm.

Where *you* come in, Joey, where you differ from all my other Saviours, is that you shattered the whole desperate farce by showing me how to laugh—at everything. The "everything" is important. Before I met you I certainly knew how to laugh, and I did laugh a great deal; but there were some things I didn't laugh at, or wouldn't laugh at, or *couldn't* laugh at. To make it brief, what I mean is this . . . once you get it, whatever "it" may be to you, you can also laugh at it. Call "it" what you like, it makes no difference. If it has reality, it's unassailable. *Also* . . . when you're uneasy about something, which means that your mind is disturbed, laugh at it! Whether it be a spook, an angel, or an invisible microbe, laugh it away! The more you laugh, the oftener you laugh, the easier it gets to be. Finally you understand why the hyena also laughs occasionally. Then you're really *there*. By the same token, you also understand why a right-thinking man, though he has had nothing to eat, will nevertheless pick his teeth.

Yes, nearing forty, a failure by all accounts—and a simpleton to boot—I gradually, almost imperceptibly, entered upon a new phase of life. Hardly aware of it, and certainly without thought or effort, I found myself entering the realm of happiness. Perhaps happiness isn't precisely the word. Perhaps I ought to call it a state of blessedness. . . . Excuse me a moment, I've got a laughing fit. Imagine two rogues like us calling ourselves blessed! Yet I can think of no lesser word that would truly describe what I mean.

How many times since we parted have your little phrases rung in my ears! "You've worked enough today, Joey, let's go out!" "Be good to yourself!" "Tomorrow's another day." "When do we eat?" "Forget about *her*, I'll find you a better one." These homely little tidbits, always delivered at the right moment, were like drops of oil lubricating a rusty machine. You, carefree soul that you were, you never bothered to write more than two pages a day; even if you were in the middle of a sentence, you stopped at the end of that second page. What wisdom! "Render unto Caesar what is Caesar's. . . ." You never got the two mixed up. The left hand always did what it was supposed to do and the right hand what the right hand was supposed to do. To make me wiser and stronger you pretended to be weak and foolish. To lift my spirits you pretended to be defeated. To make me more saintly you leaned on me so heavily that you almost broke my back. What a metaphysician! No one ever suspected that the clown, the buffoon, the rogue and the scallywag who kept everyone in stitches, who made the most solemn utterances appear ridiculous, who had no more reverence for God than for toilet paper, who could lie as easily as he could tell the truth, nobody, I say, had the least suspicion that you were exerting the greatest influence of all. Nor did you yourself know what an example you were setting me. If you did, it wasn't of much importance to you. All you seemed to be concerned about was—*never a dull moment!* The ceaseless laughter in which you enveloped us served as a veil to conceal your wonder-working powers. We laughed in blissful ignorance, never realizing that you were producing the loaves and fishes which sustained us. The only credit or acknowledgment you ever got from us, and this always behind your back, was the admission we would make to one another, in your absence —that we missed you. As Tony, my little boy, used to say after a brief absence from home, and always in a cheery voice: "We *miss*-ed you, Daddy!"

Long after you had left Paris to take up life in England, while roaming through France, roaming through Greece, roaming the streets of New York or the great stretches of the Far West, I often pulled myself up with a halt to exclaim: "Christ, if only Fred were here!" No matter how melancholy I might feel, the moment I uttered your name I would burst into laughter. Never have I summoned your image without this accompanying lift of the diaphragm. The moment I pronounced your name it was as if I had received the command to relax, to let go, to see the world for what it is. To be sure, if I think hard enough, I can recall occasions when I spotted a worried look in your eyes. Like everyone else, you had your days, days when you were not yourself. But I had only to give you a poke in the ribs to make you snap out of it. And if you said to me, as you sometimes did—always in mock solemnity, always simulating an horrendous simian despair—"Joey, things are truly desperate, there's no way out this time!"—I knew that you were all right, that you were deliberately making the picture black because the blacker it was the easier it would be to ridicule it. You were never disturbed about the big things, calamities such as war, revolution, famine and pestilence. It was the little things that got you down: the threatened loss of a job or the prospect of riding second-class in the Metro. The threat of wholesale disaster only heightened your joviality. "We'll all go down together, hurrah!" And you were perfectly right to be disturbed only about trifles. The big things always take care of themselves, as our friend Powys points out in his philosophy of "In Spite Of." To be serviceable, a real philosophy of life must show us how to deal with the irksome everyday problems, the trifles which make us fret and fume, nag and bicker with one another.

Despite your natural buoyancy and resiliency I did worry about you, I must confess, when I saw you becoming an English citizen. It was one thing, thought I to myself, to do your part (in the war) for the British who had been so good to you; it was quite another to make yourself a British subject. That you should dream of spending the rest of your life in England I regarded as nothing less than calamitous. (You probably never entertained the thought of remaining there. You probably told yourself that with a British passport you could travel about the world in greater comfort and security. Right?)

No, adaptable though you be, I had visions of you stifled and nullified in that heavy, lugubrious atmosphere. I could not picture you making the English laugh as you had made us laugh. I couldn't see you, the epicure, the gourmet, bearing up under that tasteless food the British serve three times a day. Nor could I see you switching to beer, ale and porter after years of drinking only the best French wines. (I trust you still remember that day in the Villa Seurat when we vowed never to touch *vin ordinaire* except in dire emergency!) I forgot, obviously, that you ever had your wits about you, that when you really needed something you usually managed to get it.

Anyway, seeing you standing at the foot of the stairs in the American Express office there in Barcelona, sporting that "smile at the foot of the ladder," I sensed immediately that your long residence in England hadn't diminished you in the least. I could tell at a glance that not only were you all you ever had been but that you were "Alf plus," "Alf" raised to the tenth degree. Even matrimony, which was a new and perhaps frightening experience for you, had not created a single dent in your shining armor. You were intact. Even more intact than Rimbaud was when he said he was and wasn't.

What strikes me now, looking back upon those forty-eight hours we spent together in Barcelona, is this—you had become as solid as a rock and as light as air. There are such anomalies, believe it or not. All granite, yet light as a feather. It's a conundrum I've puzzled over long and deeply. A simpler way to put it would be to say that you appeared to have become "invulnerable." Having done away with all defense mechanisms, you were immune to the "slings and arrows of outrageous fortune." A paradox? Not at all. As George Dibbern once put it—"Serve life and life will take care of you."

Here I suddenly recall one of your traits which used to baffle me in the old days. I refer to the faithful, scrupulous, punctilious way you did whatever you were bidden to do. It seemed incongruous with the rest of your nature. It went beyond the incongruous—*ridiculous* is the only word for it—when you painstakingly did the wrong thing, *because*

you had been told to do it. And what was your famous
rejoinder, did I happen to call your attention to the fact?
"That's *their* look-out, Joey!" So saying, you considered
yourself absolved. More, you *enjoyed* the situation. Since
the world is run by nitwits, you insinuated, why not be an
out and out nitwit when occasion provides? *Bref,* never
throw pearls before swine! Quite naturally, you never made
the least effort to improve your position. The bottom rung
suited you just as much as the top. You seemed content,
and I am certain you *were* content, with whatever post was
assigned you. If you had been asked to do nothing but
empty the waste paper basket you would have done it with
good grace. If there were complaint to make, it would be
that there weren't enough waste paper baskets to empty.
"Somebody has to do it. Why not *me?*" That was your attitude. And it was the correct one, let no one gainsay it. But
what a dope I was to be concerned about your nonchalance!
Or to presume that you were meant for better uses.

Yes, one glance at you standing at the bottom of the
stairs and I could see how right you were, and always had
been, about everything. You had not only survived the
worst ordeals, you had triumphed over them. You were
never aware that they *were* ordeals, that's the blessed point.
"What a darlint of a man!" as my wife Evie puts it. Hungry,
you simply foraged for victuals; weary, you sought a comfortable bed and flopped into it; in need of a lay, you got
yourself one by hook or crook, even if it meant betraying
a good friend. Not that you were a heartless son-of-a-bitch!
Not at all. You had other ways of demonstrating your
friendship than by observing the punctilios of etiquette
and convention. Caught red-handed, you invariably offered
both cheeks to be slapped. You were never reluctant to
take the punishment you merited. In fact, you *demanded*
your punishment. To you it was like balancing the ledger, I
suppose.

Ah, how little the world understands these matters! It is
so easy to regard such behavior as cowardly, spineless,
meek or abject. But all this only serves to remind me of the
busybodies we were then surrounded by. Each one was out
to save the other's soul. All struggling to do good—and
making such a mess of it. And there you were, in the dead

center of all the commotion, assiduously lapping up the crumbs. You even helped add to the confusion, since confusion was the order of the day. The one thing you never did was to give advice. Instead you laughed, or else you would mumble something in German, a dictum of Goethe's which you had fabricated on the spot. Sometimes you deliberately slammed the door on a helpless idiot. If he came back for more the next day, and if that day you happened to be in a rollicking mood, you would soothe his injured feelings by borrowing money of him or making him take you to lunch. What divine remedies you made use of!

Strolling down the Rambla that afternoon, the wine and food rolling around in our distended guts, I had the impression that a playful dolphin was swimming beside me. Or should I say—a celestial porpoise? You were so utterly relaxed, so resilient: you no longer belonged to the world of land animals. Addled with ecstasy, you dove into the breakers, rode the waves, flapped your fins, rolled in the surf. All flip and froth, come Christmas or St. Bartholomew's Eve. *Homo naturalis,* if ever I saw one.

"The mission of man on earth is to remember. . . ." Sailing down the Rambla I perceived how marvelously you had taken the phrase to heart.

"Not till you have sacrificed everything you have acquired will remembrance come back to you." You put those words in Iris Day's mouth.* But you also lived them.

Did not Iris Day also say—"From the point of view of the individual, it does not matter whether one is, by fate, on the right or the wrong side." How well you have illustrated that truth! In the first war you were on one side and in the second war on the other side. And if tomorrow there should be another war it will find you on the side which fate has chosen for you. You will have no compunctions about killing the wrong man. When it's time for the bloodletting to begin, what difference does it make on which side one is ranged? If fools weren't constantly taking sides there would never be a war. And the greatest fool is he who thinks that God is on the side of the big battalions. No, to

* See *The Renegade,* by Alfred Perlès. George Allen and Unwin, Ltd., London, 1943.

come back to Iris Day and the sublime point of view, neither victory nor defeat matters. What matters is how you
live it through.

It wasn't just memories which made us so supremely
happy those two days and nights in Barcelona. It was
something more. To capture the "remembrance of things
past" one has first to attain a state of bliss. The past doesn't
resurrect for the man of good memory the way it does for
an innocent soul. The one who truly remembers is the one
who sees back with the eyes of God. He has first to become
dead to the past before it can come alive again. No one
enters the realm of experience with eyes wide open. We
enter blindly, and we awaken to discover that it was other
than we imagined it to be. Experience, in other words, is
merely an eye opener. As we shuffle off the load we have
accumulated along the way, as we make more and more
sacrifices—burn away the dross—we become more and
more at one with each other, with God, with the whole
world. Losing all that seemed so precious to us we regain
the Source, where there is no longer any difference between
thou and me. When tomorrow is no better than yesterday,
and sin no different from goodness, one is able and ready
to remember everything . . . and one is also ready and
able to *forget* everything.

On the beach at Sitges, with no pail and shovel, no toy
balloon, not even a stick of candy, you were *quand-même*
the perfect picture of a child, happier a thousandfold, I'm
sure, than when you were a child in years. It was one of
those *fin de siècle* days such as Renoir, Pisarro, Seurat have
immortalized. Even the waves seemed immobilized under
the spell of enchantment that reigned. That evening, back
on the Rambla again, we sat down to have our last few
drinks together. Our laughter, though still boisterous, was
verging on tears. Everything was still droll, hallucinatingly
droll. Then the shoeshine men appeared, first singly like
sluggish bottle-flies, then in pairs, then in droves. Twice
we had our shoes shined with only a vague sense of what
was happening. Events were taking place as in a dream,
one of those delicious dreams which one slips in or out
of at will. We were dreaming back, I suppose, to other
dream days. There were thousands of such days, and we

had infinite time in which to relive them. It was an interval
reminiscent of the Devachan we used to conjure up in the
Villa Seurat. The same cigars, the same good black coffee,
the same wonderful lays—only dream cigars, dream coffee,
dream girls. Thus the Rambla, the conversation, the laughter, the shoeshine men coming and going. It was the sound
of hammers pounding our soles and heels which brought
us rudely back to reality. There they were, those uncon-
scionable brigands, working on our hooves like a pair of
blacksmiths. Had they asked permission to mutilate our
well-shod shoes with those flimsy pieces of rubber? Perhaps.
Perhaps we had said yes, dreaming that we were horses
rather than butterflies. The waiters, however, had never
entered the trance. They were furious, first at the shoe-
blacks and then at us for being such incredible fools. The
climax came when you laughingly suggested that we order
a round of drinks for the brigands. That was a little too
much, even for a Spaniard. It was time to go. The dream
was shattered.

I can still see you walking up the stairs of your hotel—
which turned out *not* to be the Hotel Vienna—and as you
wave good-by you're still doubled up with laughter. Every
few steps you turn around and pause, as if uncertain
whether to go on to bed or run down and rejoin us.

We had agreed, in parting, to renew the reunion a few
months later—in Wells. No doubt it was at the London air-
port that you came to meet us, but in my mind it will always
be Paddington Station. Anyway, there you are, dressed like
a bloody Englishman, with pipe, brogans, tweeds, rolled
umbrella and the perennial *imperméable*. You talk with a
different voice, like one born and bred in the British Isles.
You seem so very much at home, even more so than when
you were living in Paris. You would like us to stay over-
night in London and see a bit of the town. But we want to
get to Wells, the quicker the better.

It's a long, hot ride to Wells, with several changes of
train, but that doesn't bother us in the least. Along the way
we catch glimpses of those unbelievably sleek, contented
cows which stand up to their flanks in clover. What luxu-

riant warmth and moisture! How green the fields! it's old England all right, no doubt about it.

What I was not prepared for was the Cathedral. Nor your "chambers" flanking the green. Nor the marvelous French wines that were waiting to be sampled once we had found the key to the innkeeper's heart.

But the Cathedral . . . It's the first cathedral I've ever fallen in love with. (One doesn't fall in love with Chartres, it's too sublime.) Immediately I glimpsed those bizarre figures plastered over the façade it happened. One look at them and I was under their spell. In some unaccountable way they belonged to the England I knew from my boys' books. They were *invraisemblable,* as is all English history to me. Their atrociously weather-beaten air suited them perfectly too. Floodlit, they were altogether hallucinating. Had King Arthur himself come sailing out of the front portals I could not have been more spellbound.

Certainly there was nothing gay or lively about Wells itself, but then I had never entertained any illusions of the sort. The two or three pubs we visited now and then had all the charm needed to compensate for the lack of more sinful enticements. For me the pub spelled civilization. English civilization. It told me more about the British than any other institution I can think of. Even if it seemed a bit like going to chapel, even if the beer and ale were detestable (to *my* taste), even if the talk that went on smacked of dementia, the warm, cozy, intimate air of the pub was definitely most agreeable. Far better, thought I to myself, than hanging oneself by a rope in a dirty garret. . . . The day the pubs are done away with England is doomed. She's doomed anyhow, but that's neither here nor there.

After a few days of it I understood why you refused to think of making Wells your permanent dwelling place. Either you would be obliged to become a member of the parish or you would have to shoot yourself. Wells is a place to return to, in one's dotage, when life has nothing more to offer than to open a shop and sell souvenirs to tourists.

And now, though I fear it will make Anne, your dear wife, think me highly ungrateful, I must confess that it was a mistake to have made that excursion to Stratford on

Avon. The trip to Wookey Hole, only a stone's throw away, was quite in order. To have skipped Glastonbury, though, was a horrible mistake. (I am now knee-deep in that prodigious "romance"* of Friar John's which Glastonbury inspired.) Having visited El Greco's home in Toledo and the Rabelais homestead at La Devinière, having walked through the forest of beeches which once sheltered the Admirable Ruysbroeck, Stratford on Avon was a letdown. What I shall remember most about Shakespeare's birthplace is that fool of a waiter in the hostelry nearby who insisted on acting the part of Edward VII when he was obviously neither an actor nor a waiter, nor even a funeral director.

The other day I picked up a book which opens like this: *"Au-dessus du chemin que chacun suit dans la vie, il y a un chemin invisible que nous parcourons sans le savoir . . ."*** It's a book I intend to send you soon, one I am certain you will enjoy reading. I picked it up, as I say, and intrigued by the opening lines, I swallowed it at one gulp. All the while I kept thinking of you. To be sure, it is not a great book. But it is one of those books which, if you happen to be properly attuned when you come upon it, echoes your inmost thoughts on every page. A "companionate" book, I would call it. Though replete with confessions, which so often can be frightfully dull, you soon find yourself immersed in experiences of an illuminating nature. What captivated me was the author's ability to distill from even the most trivial incidents an incredibly meaningful potion. The book closes on this note: *"Heureux les hommes pleins de sérénité qui n'ont aucun retour en arrière et ne voudraient pas changer la face du monde pour rendre plus heureux ceux qu'ils aiment!"*

But it was along about the middle of the book, in the midst of a passage dealing with that other world which lies behind the supposedly real world, that I had the most wonderful recollections of certain intuitive flashes connect-

---

* *A Glastonbury Romance,* by John Cowper Powys.
** *Confessions sur les femmes, l'opium, l'amour,* etc. by Maurice Magre.

ed with the subject of prophecy. I suppose I ought to quote first. Here is the passage. . . .

"*J'étais un pauvre aveugle, un misérable sourd. Je ne connaissais que l'envers des choses. J'avais jusqu'ici traversé la vie dans le mensonge at même dans la stupidité. Derrière ce que je croyais être le monde vrai, j'entrevoyais un autre monde, un double plus subtil et plus beau. Mais comment l'atteindre? N'allait-il pas s'effacer? Toute mon education était à refaire. Je devais revenir à l'age de cinq ans, apprendre à lire dans l'alphabet de l'âme, essayer de déchiffrer le livre magnifique de la mort.*"

The connection? you ask. I wonder if I can give it. . . . You may recall that during our trip abroad I wrote you a number of times about the discussions I had with Dr. de Fontbrune of Périgeueux. The subject was always Nostradamus, and no doubt I bored the shit out of you. But this is the point, and it is a most important one to me. . . . After several very long talks with Dr. de Fontbrune, after one in particular which took place on the banks of the Dordogne at Les Eyzies, I was seized with such a certitude about that "*chemin invisible que nous parcourons sans le savoir*" that my head felt as if it were constellated with scintillating gems. The world we know and accept as the real world became as transparent as gauze. You know what happens when you isolate and examine any particle of matter, be it a grain of wheat, a fingernail, or a tiny gem —you cannot help becoming intensely aware that a supreme and inscrutable Intelligence is manifesting itself. You sense an order, a purpose, a beauty, a logic to which you are ordinarily blind. Likewise, when you dwell on the prophetic, you come to realize that there is an invisible pattern to the events which mold our destiny, and that history, philosophy, science, art, religion yield but a distorted, meaningless, even ridiculous image of this divine web. But the most interesting aspect of this experience, this lifting of the veil, is that all desire to modify, hasten or retard events is nullified. What is is, what will be will be, and that suffices. Merely to recognize, if only for a moment, that there *is* a greater plan, enables one to abdicate. In abdicating one is not removed from the stream of life, even mentally; one plunges in more deeply, more wholeheartedly, that is the curious thing. All that is sacrificed is one's limited, egocentric view of life, the view which caused one to swim against the current instead of with it. One is also made acutely aware that history can never offer anything but a *backward* view of things. One is convinced that neither a backward nor a forward view is of the least importance. *"Before Abraham was I am."* It's on that fulcrum you come to rest. Denying the world will not rid us of it. Separating spirit and reality only makes one hopelessly divided. The visible and the invisible are one. The mind that grasps this ceases to struggle. It is no longer life and death, but life in death and death in life, the two joined like Siamese twins and making for something that is beyond the meaning of either. It follows inevitably that the one and only thing to do is to live as if the Kingdom of Heaven were already here. . . .

But enough. This is getting too serious. Besides, all I wanted to tell you, or urge you, is to continue doing as little as possible, even as little good as possible. For, if any have succeeded better in fucking up the world than the evildoers it is the do-gooders, the right-thinkers, the pious frauds.

And now, Joey, knowing how exceedingly modest, exceedingly reticent, exceedingly delicate you are about revealing your inner state, I can only whisper to you that I look upon you as one of the chosen ones. You have taken elaborate pains to conceal the fact, but truth will out. At any rate, your friend Henry who writes you thus wishes to testify that he has learned more from your crazy antics, your irrepressible laughter, your insouciance and seeming irresponsibility than from all the learned tomes he has devoured. Over the years he has been scrapping excess baggage, but never fast enough, never rigorously enough. He has learned to kill the Buddha, but he has yet to slaughter a host of lesser evils. He is weary of getting there slowly, yet he does not wish to get there like a rocket either.

Remember the swans (at Wells) that arrived punctually at 4:00 P.M. every day for their tea and muffins? They even rang the bell to announce themselves. That's the sort of instinctive wisdom we all might cultivate to advantage. I mean, not just to be on hand for tea at four sharp, but to be there ringing the bell with our beaks. I believe you purposely invited me to witness this extraordinary spectacle in order to give me a last lesson. *The lesson?* This . . . Until it's time for tea what better than to sail up and down on the bosom of time, preening my feathers in the golden sunlight, and, while dreaming, dream true. Come tea time, ring the bell . . . arms or no arms. The swans have been doing it for generations. Why not yours truly? Maybe with a bit of practice I shall be able to ring for a Westphalian ham straight from Jerusalem! There is one thing nobody can dispute—the swans have an inner certitude about tea time which is nothing short of miraculous. Set all the clocks in the village wrong, the swans of Wells will still arrive at four *punkt* for tea and muffins. If a swan knows that much unerringly, you may be certain it knows a lot more.

The point of all this is, Joey, that it was you who taught me how to tell tea time from historical time and sidereal time and space-time as well as all the other no account times. And now it's time to call a halt. Be good to yourself, and remember—do just as little as possible! "Piss warm and drink cold," as Trimalchio says, "because our mother the earth is in the middle, made round like an egg, and has all good things in herself, like a honeycomb."

Big Sur, California
May 19, 1954

BALZAC AND HIS DOUBLE

IN HIS BOOK on St. Francis of Assisi, Chesterton endeavors to put his finger on the weakness of that sect whose members styled themselves "the true sons of St. Francis"—the Fraticelli—and whose goal it was to carry out the complete program of St. Francis. "What was the matter with these people," writes Chesterton, "was that they were mystics; mystics and nothing else but mystics; mystics and not Christians; mystics and not men. They rotted away because, in the most exact sense, they would not listen to reason. And St. Francis, however wild and romantic his gyrations, always hung on to reason by one invisible and indestructible hair." In the *History of Magic* by Eliphas Levi we have a similar indictment of the mystics; they are condemned and vituperated because they are extremists. In his autobiographical study called *Louis Lambert,* Balzac, who was a believer in the esoteric doctrine—too catholic a spirit to be a Catholic—gives us a picture of the conflict between the angel in man and the flesh which throws a different light upon the dangers which are supposed to attend the mystic in his unbridled desire for union with the infinite all.

Who was Louis Lambert? He was not only, as the story relates, *le copain,* the chum, the alter ego, he was Balzac's own real self, the angelic self which was killed in the struggle with the world. At that moment in Louis Lambert's life when, as Balzac says, he perceived in him "the struggle of the mind reacting on itself," he adds—"at this stage of weakness and strength, of childish grace and superhuman

34

powers, Louis Lambert is the creature who, more than any other, gave me a poetical and truthful image of the being we call an angel." When in his fifteenth year he parts from his double at the College of Vendôme, he says: "You will live, but I shall die. If I can, I will come back to you." In the story he does come back, to find Louis mad, but in life he never came back. In taking leave of himself in this strangely prophetic manner it is interesting to note that Balzac immediately proceeds to give a physical description of his double, an exact description, including Louis' height, adding significantly: *"he grew no more!"* In the midst of his narrative, in an interlude of two short paragraphs wherein he makes a transition from the known life of his double to the subsequent and imagined life of the mystic who rotted away in the flesh, Balzac remarks that in describing Louis' boyhood he is depicting "the unknown life to which I owe the only happy hours, the only pleasant memories, of my early days. Excepting these two years I have had nothing but annoyances and weariness."

The book is an attempt on Balzac's part to justify himself not only to the world, but to himself. It is a study of the ordeal and crucifixion of a genius, a defense of the real Balzac whom the world refused to acknowledge. It is an outcry against the critics for failing to discern in the novelist the more important attributes of thinker, visionary, prophet. (Referring to Louis Lambert he says, "I think we may deplore in him a genius equal to Pascal, Lavoisier or Laplace." And elsewhere in the book: "his philosophical speculations ought undoubtedly to gain him recognition as one of the great thinkers who have appeared at wide intervals among men to reveal to them the bare skeleton of some science to come. . . .") But it was above all the failure to detect "the angel" which reduced Balzac to despair and moved him to write this harrowing study of frustration. In the story it is the angel, which, at the price of reason and sanity, is finally liberated; but in life it is the angel which is destroyed in order that the artist may triumph. What Chesterton said of St. Francis was also true of Balzac—he too had the ability to hang on to reason by that one invisible and indestructible hair. But was it worth it? If Louis Lambert may be said to succumb to madness—

and even this admission is questionable, if one reads Balzac's judgment carefully—he, Balzac, the man of indomitable courage and will, certainly succumbed to a worse fate. He succumbed to fame and glory. The soaring ambitions of genius brought him nothing but trials and tribulations, brought him to the grave prematurely, at the very moment when he had hoped to sit back and reap the harvest of his tremendous labors. Even the great love, to which he struggled for seventeen years to give a solid, secure pediment, was snatched from him. He had given her in marriage the living cadaver of himself.

Just as *Seraphita* was written for Madame Hanska, his ideal love, so *Louis Lambert* was written for his "Dilecta," Madame de Berny, who had been to him not only a devoted mistress, but a mother as well, for Balzac had never known a mother's love. Da Vinci had two mothers; Goethe had the best mother a genius could possibly have; but Balzac was deprived of an affection and tenderness which he needed possibly more than either Goethe or da Vinci. His life at the College of Vendôme was a nightmare. Reserved, secretive, oversensitive, precocious, misunderstood by masters and pupils alike, he became indifferent to the world about and was forced to retire into himself—to commune with the angels. This sense of loneliness developed with the years, despite the fame and renown which he tasted early in his career. In his letters he refers frequently to a secret which no one, not even Madame Hanska, to whom he confesses this on occasion, will ever penetrate. At the very threshold of his career, in the year 1828, he writes that there are people who die without the doctor's ever being able to say what it was that carried them off. The lack of maternal tenderness, the estrangement, the hatred which was shown him by his mother, left an indelible mark upon him. His incarceration in the College of Vendôme only served to stimulate the already premature development of his spiritual nature, the *man* lagged behind. In fact, the man in him was never fully realized. Balzac, throughout his life, not only felt himself to be an exile and a prisoner, but deliberately made his life a prison, in order to punish himself for a crime which he had never committed. His dismal failure as a writer, throughout the years of apprenticeship when he signed false names to his work, testifies not only to the slow development common to great geniuses but points also to the powers of frustration born of his crippled affections.

In *Louis Lambert* Balzac gives us the genesis of a giant moth doomed to perish in a flame of light. To grasp the true significance of this study it should be borne in mind not only that the poet was murdered at school (where all the poets are murdered!) but that the date, June-July, 1832, given for this story, represents his thirty-third year! Long before the great financial disaster, which served him as an excuse to make himself a Martyr of Work, Balzac realized that he was destined for a Purgatorial existence. In that harrowing letter which Louis Lambert writes from his miserable garret in Paris, Balzac gives the clue to his own secret hopes and disillusionment. "Compelled to live in himself alone," he writes, "having no one to share his subtle raptures, he may have hoped to solve the problem of his destiny by a life of ecstasy, adopting an almost vegetative attitude, like an anchorite of the early church, and abdicating the empire of the intellectual world." This vegetative life which he was forbidden to enjoy Balzac had tasted as a boy; it was this normal desire for natural growth, for a growth which would have altered the whole tenor of his life, which might have permitted him to become a seer rather than a novelist, it was this hunger for the opportunity to permit his real self to flower, that militated against his early development as a writer. The real Balzac is absent from the first forty volumes; it is a ghost writing. The real Balzac is still enwrapped in the chrysalis which he had spun about himself in the College of Vendôme. What a tragic, fateful moment it was when, as a boy of fourteen, Balzac was returned to his parents by the masters of the College as a walking somnambulist, an embryonic monster of thought suffering from a *"congestion de lumière."* Even when he throws himself into life, when outwardly he seems to be fulfilling the role of a young man who is in love, who is acquiring a vocation, who is studying life, the spell in which he had wrapped himself is so strong that he has no sense of his gifts, still less of his destiny, but struggles like a worm in its cocoon in order to liberate himself from his self-imposed prison. The young man who makes his appearance in the world, who conquers by a single glance of his magnetic eye, is simply the ghost which, by sheer force of will, succeeds in bursting the wrappings of a dormant soul. In *Louis Lambert* Balzac depicts himself as the dreamer who succeeds in detaching himself from his body. In seeking to violate the laws of nature his triumph is nullified, because, as he is later to know from experience, in order to overcome the world it is first necessary to accept it. As an artist he does overcome the world, by making it "transparent," but to become the artist he had first to understand the submission of the will. The submission or surrender of the artist is only the first step in the path of renunciation. That Balzac realized the nature of the conflict in himself is evident from the work which follows shortly after *Louis Lambert*—*Seraphita*. Between the themes of these two books there is a void which can be likened to a desert in which psychologically, or spiritually, the whole of Balzac's life is passed. Unlike the saints and mystics whom he revered, Balzac never returned from the desert. His immense production is simply a monologue, a wilderness of the soul's anguish in which the wanderer is lost.

It was only when the artist in him awakened, when he had accepted his duality, understood his role, that Balzac, by a prodigious metamorphosis, succeeded in making the world itself into a chrysalis and, from the depths of his imagination, gathers the wings which will permit him to fly beyond the world while remaining ever securely imprisoned *in* it. When he says of Louis Lambert that "the point to which most thinkers reach at last was to him the starting point whence his brain was to set out one day in search of new worlds of knowledge," did he not mean that in his stupendous vegetative slumber he had exhausted the whole world of the intellect, that though still a boy, he nevertheless stood on the frontier of a new way of life? And that as a man he was condemned to be a prisoner of the age in which he was born? What is the meaning of the words which follow on the above? "Though as yet he [Louis Lambert] knew it not, he had made for himself the most exacting life possible, and the most insatiably greedy. *Merely to live,* was he not compelled to be perpetually casting nutriment into the gulf he had opened in himself?" *What gulf?* Had he already franchised the barriers of his living tomb? All his life Balzac was promising to bring forth an essay on *"les forces humaines."* All his life he struggles to deliver the secret of that imaginary document which Louis Lambert wrote at college—*Traité sur la Volonté*—and which was destroyed by the ignorant and insensitive headmaster. In *La Peau de Chagrin* (wherein we also have glimpses of his boyhood) he again gives expression to his obsession when he writes that he believed he had a great thought to express, a system to establish, a science to elucidate. Of the visions which he had at school he says that they gave to his eyes the faculty of seeing the intimate, the quintessential nature of things. Through them his heart was prepared *"pour les magies."* And then he adds, as a final tribute to the effect of these sublime visions: "they inscribed in my brain a book wherein I could read what I had to express; they gave to my lips the power of spontaneous utterance." "From the very beginning," says Ernst-Robert Curtius, "Balzac's life is dominated by a mystic star, by a ray of light emanating from the higher worlds." It is with this vision of greater things, this vision of a life as yet unknown to us, that Balzac progresses through the world, devouring everything in sight, creating a vast panorama peopled with his own figures, and yet eternally dissatisfied, because nothing the earth had to offer could compensate for that life which he was denied. The *Treatise on the Will,* which is symbolically destroyed by the ignorant headmaster, never materializes into the promised essay *"sur les forces humanies,"* unless, as one well might, we consider *La Comédie Humaine* itself as an elaborate elucidation of the subject. The embryonic Balzac, who eventually became a Colossus, was a living travesty of the Will. In *Seraphita* he reveals the true function of the Will: it is the desire to rise, to go beyond the limits of the self, to expand in the Infinite Self.

Balzac, the writer, deflected his great will in order to subjugate the world. Both the Poet and the Pythagoras in him were doomed: the Colossus was engulfed in the sands of his own creation. The whole vast edifice of his work appears, ultimately, like a Gargantuan effort to bury the secret which gnawed at his vitals. At the age of twenty-three, still inchoate, still paralyzed, though aware of the possession of a tremendous force, he writes to his "Dilecta" concerning the doctrines of Leibnitz, arrested by the thought that everything in the world, organic and inorganic, is possessed with life. He avers that even marble may be said to have ideas—"extraordinarily confused, however." He confides that he too would like to obtain "solidity, durability, immobility." It was from this crude block of marble, Curtius writes, that the gigantic edifice of *La Comédie Humaine* had to be hewn. This is tantamount to saying that it was created out of the will rather than the flame. For Balzac the Will was supreme—*"le roi des fluides,"* as he put it. It was the Will which enabled him to bridge the gulf which had opened in himself and into which he flung his great work.

His whole life was a contradiction of his philosophy: it was the most stupid, aborted life that any intelligent man ever lived. What a strange tribute it is that he makes to his double in *Louis Lambert!* After making a cryptic acknowledgment of his indebtedness to his alter ego, he says: "and this is not all I have borrowed from him . . . this present volume is intended as a modest monument, a broken column, to commemorate the life of the man who bequeathed to me all he had to leave—his thoughts." In *Seraphita* he gives us his opinion of the grand edifice which he created. "Books are human actions in death," he says. From this solid, durable unshakeable edifice, from the crude block of marble out of which his great work was fashioned, the real Balzac never emerged. Of the three great stages on the mystic path he knew only the first two, and these in reverse order—*la vie purgative et la vie illuminative. La vie unitive,* which is the grand theme pervading his works, he never knew. Like Pythagoras he knew the secret of number: like Virgil he foresaw a world to come; like Dante he proclaimed the inner doctrine, and in the book which is least known of all his work, *Seraphita,* he gave us this doctrine, and there it lies buried. His intuition was cosmic, his will was titan-like, his energy inexhaustible, his nature truly protean, and yet he was unable to emancipate himself. The study of society and the psychology of the individual, which form the material of the novel in European literature, served to create the illusory world of facts and things which dominate the neurotic life that began with the 19th century and is now reaching its end in the drama of schizophrenia. At the back of it is the Will, reducing through the powers of analysis all life to ashes. Balzac was himself aware of the disease which is killing us. It is the mind which is poisoning us, he says somewhere. *"La vie est un feu qu'il faut couvrir de cendres; penser, c'est ajouter la flamme au feu."* Dostoievski gave expression to the conflict even more forcibly. Indeed, it is with him that the novel comes to an end, for after him there are no longer any individuals to write about, nor is there any longer a society which may be said to possess a body. Proust and Joyce epitomize the dissolution of our world in their great epics. With Lawrence the novel becomes a vehicle for the Apocalyptic visions which will occupy us for the next few hundred years, as our world fades out in blood and tears.

"Werther," says Balzac, "is a slave of desire; Louis Lambert was an enslaved soul." A tremendous admission, *shattering,* if Balzac is to be identified, as he intended, with his double. Despite the most gigantic efforts ever man made, the real Balzac did not grow an inch from the time he left his prison at Vendôme to enter the world. Adopting the Purgatorial life, after having experienced the joys and splendors of illumination, taking up his cross and nailing himself to it, he nevertheless was refused the reward of blossoming into a miraculous rose. He knew—he gave expression to it several times in his work—that the real miracle happens within, yet he persisted in looking for it without. His life was devoid of joy or hope; he is the symbol of the convict condemned to a life of hard labor. At that stage of division wherein he detects the angel in Louis Lambert he erects the tombstone over his own grave. As Louis Lambert he sinks deeper and deeper into the world of Maya; as Balzac he sinks into the morass of the world of things, the world of desire which is inappeasable. Louis Lambert gives up the struggle with the world in order to commune with the angels, but unlike Swedenborg, he forgets to leave the door open. Balzac struggles with the world in order to down the angel in himself. He rails and fumes

against the world for its inability or unwillingness to understand and appreciate him, but the confusion he precipitated
was of his own making. His life was as disordered, confused
and chaotic as the bedeviled proofs of his manuscripts, the
like of which the world has never seen, except in the work
of the insane. He beclouded the real issue with a smoke
screen of words; he fought like a madman to blind his own
eyes to the path which he was ordained to follow. The
world has been kind and at the same time cruel to him, in
the very measure of duality and antagonism which he created. It has accepted him as one of the greatest of human
geniuses; it has remained ignorant of the real goal which
he set himself. He wanted fame, glory, recognition: he received them. He wanted riches, possessions, power over
men: he obtained all of these. He wanted to create a world
of his own: he did. But the true life which he secretly
desired to live was denied him—because one cannot have
one foot in one world and the other in another. He had not
learned the lesson of Renunciation: he had renounced the
world, not to abdicate, but to conquer. In his moments of
illumination he perceived the truth, but he was never able
to live according to his vision. For him, as he permits
Seraphita to say with blinding clarity, it is true that it was
a Light such as kills the man who is not prepared to receive
it. Towards the end of the book he "comes back" to Louis
and as he watches him with uncanny tenseness, waiting
eagerly for a word to fall from his lips after the unbearable
suspense of prolonged silence, what is it he puts in Louis'
mouth as the first utterance? THE ANGELS ARE WHITE!
The effect of this utterance, when the reader comes upon
it in the natural course of the narrative, is indescribable.
Even the illusion of being himself affected by these words is
dissipated by the stark reality which Balzac gives them. It
is like saying *truth is truth!* THE ANGELS ARE WHITE
—this is the utmost Balzac can think to say in his assumed
madness, after days, weeks and months of standing at the
mantelpiece rubbing one leg against the other and piercing
with dead eyes the veils of the Infinite. *The angels are white!*
It is madder than anything Nijinsky wrote in his diary. It is
pure madness, white as the light itself, and yet so thoroughly
sane that it seems like a Euclidean statement of identity. It

is the reduction of all his Pythagorean wisdom to an image which is hallucinating. Number, substance, weight, measure, motion—all are consumed here to give an image which is more meaningful than meaning itself.

In the limited illustrated edition of the book published by Dent, London, there is, in addition to the asinine preface by George Saintsbury, an etching of Louis inspired by this phrase. I mention it because I was astonished, after having read the story several times, to find on flipping the pages that the artist had portrayed Louis in a manner absolutely different from that which I had imagined from memory. In my own mind I always saw Louis standing at the mantelpiece in a trance, but—*looking like a horse!* On re-reading Balzac's description of him, as he appeared at this moment, I find that my image is fairly correct. But what strikes me now is that the person I really had in mind, *Louis'* double, as it were, is Nijinsky. And this is not really so strange as it may at first seem. For if ever there was a flesh and blood image of Balzac's extraordinary lunatic it is the dancer Nijinsky. He too left the earth while still alive, never to return again. He too became a horse equipped with chimerical wings. The horse, let us not forget, even when he has no wings, flies. So too, every genius, when he is truly inspired, mounts the winged steed to write his name in the heavens. How often, in reading Nijinsky's *Diary,* have I thought of Mademoiselle de Villenoix's words! "Louis," says this guardian angel who never deserted her lover, "must no doubt appear to be mad, but he is not, if the term mad ought only to be used in speaking of those whose brain is for some unknown cause diseased, and who can show no reason in their actions. Everything in my husband is perfectly balanced. He has succeeded in detaching himself from his body and discerns us under some other aspect —what it is, I know not. . . . To other men he seems insane; to me, living as I do in his mind, his ideas are quite lucid. I follow the road his spirit travels; and though I do not know every turning, I can reach the goal with him." Wholly aside from the question of whether Louis Lambert was mad or not, aside from the question of what constitutes madness, which will always remain a mystery, the attitude preserved throughout by this guardian angel is in itself worthy of the deepest attention. Perhaps, in depicting the devotion of this extraordinary woman, Balzac was stressing the great need for affection, understanding, sympathy and recognition which every artist demands and which Balzac more than most men stood in want of all his life. In one of his letters, I believe it is, he says that he has known neither a spring nor a summer, but that he looked forward to enjoying a ripe autumn. He looked forward above all to a consummation of his labors through love. Over and over again, in his writings, we have this announcement of a tremendous hope. Immediately he saw Mademoiselle de Villenoix Louis "discerned the angel within." "His passion," says Balzac, "became a gulf into which he threw everything." In his first letter to her, a letter doubtless very similar to the early ones which Balzac wrote Madame Hanska, Louis expressed himself thus: ". . . my life will be in your hands, for I love you; *and to me, the hope of being loved is life!*" And then, as Balzac must himself have felt when he was wooing Madame Hanska, Louis adds: "If you had rejected me, all was over for me."

Here let me give a rapid summary of the narrative, as it is given in the book. . . .

Louis Lambert is the son of a poor tanner, an only child who is adored by his parents.* The parents, being of modest means, are unable to pay the sum required to obtain a substitute for their son, as substitutes for the army at that time (the early nineteenth century) were scarce. The only means of evading conscription was to have Louis become a priest. And so, at ten years of age, Louis is sent to his maternal uncle, a parish priest in a small town on the Loire, not far from Blois. In the second paragraph of his story Balzac launches into an account of Louis' passion for books. He began, it would seem, at the age of five by reading the Old and the New Testaments . . . "and these two books, including so many books, had sealed his fate." During the school holidays Louis devours everything in sight, "feeding indiscriminately on religious works, history, philosophy and physics." For lack of other material he often turns to the dictionaries. "The analysis of a word, its

* This is the most singular distortion, it is interesting to notice, which Balzac makes in recounting the story of his double's boyhood.

physiognomy and history, would be to Lambert matter for long dreaming . . . What a fine book might be written of the life and adventures of a word!" Of the two words which Balzac singles out for mention, curiously, one is "true" and the other "flight." In three years Louis Lambert had assimilated the contents of all that was worth reading in his uncle's library. His memory was prodigious. "He remembered with equal exactitude the ideas he had derived from reading, and those which had occurred to him in the course of meditation or conversation. Indeed, he had every form of memory—for places, for names, for words, things and faces. He not only recalled any object at will, but he saw them in his mind, situated, lighted and colored as he had originally seen them . . . He could remember, as he said, not merely the position of a sentence in the book where he had met with it, but the frame of mind he had been in at remote dates. . . ." Louis is depicted as one who "had transferred all his activities to thinking," as one who was drawn towards the mysteries, one fascinated by the abyss. He had a "taste for the things of heaven," a predilection, Balzac remarks, which was disastrous, if Louis' life is to be measured by ordinary standards. After the Bible came the reading of Saint Theresa and Madame Guyon. "This line of study, this peculiar taste, elevated his heart, purified, ennobled it, gave him an appetite for the divine nature, and suggested to him the almost womanly refinement of feeling which is instinctive in great men. . . ." At fourteen Louis leaves his uncle to enter the College of the Oratorians at Vendôme, where he was maintained at the expense of Madame de Staël who, forbidden to come within forty leagues of Paris, was in the habit of spending several months of her banishment on an estate near Vendôme. Impressed by the boy's unusual powers of mind Madame de Staël hoped to save Louis from the necessity of serving either the Emperor or the Church. During the three years he spent at the College, however, Louis never heard a word from his benefactress. Madame de Staël, in fact, dies on the very day that Louis, who had set out on foot from Blois to see her, arrived in Paris.

The life at the College is like a miniature description of Hell. "The punishments originally invented by the Society of Jesus," says Balzac, "as alarming to the moral as to the physical man, were still in force in all the integrity of the original code." Visits by the parents were extremely infrequent, holidays away from the school were forbidden; once a pupil entered his prison he never left it until his studies were terminated. The lack of physical comforts, the bad sanitation, the meager prison diet, the frequent beatings, the refined tortures inflicted by masters and pupils alike, the stupidity and bigotry of the life, the isolation, all tended to demoralize and devitalize any one with promise, and particularly a sensitive being, such as Louis Lambert. Balzac describes himself as then being twelve years of age. What the effect of such a life must have been, for his sensitive soul, can best be understood by the description of his emotions upon hearing the announcement of Louis' arrival at the College. "I can compare it with nothing but my first reading of *Robinson Crusoe,*" he says. From the first he felt sympathy (sic!) with the boy whose temperament had some points of likeness to his own. "At last I was to have a companion in daydreams and meditations!" In this naked description of the split in his psyche Balzac reveals to us the true nature of his liberation. *At last!* Like a cry of desperation.*

The physical description of Louis Lambert which Balzac gives at this point is remarkable for the resemblance to his own self. He speaks glowingly of "the prophetic brow," of the extraordinary eyes which bespoke the existence of a soul. Though he had not the ordinary strength which permitted him to rival the others in sports, Louis was possessed of a mysterious power of will which he could summon on occasion and which was capable of defying the united strength of his comrades. He speaks of the wealth of ideas, the poetry, that lay hidden in Louis' brain and heart, commenting on it in strangely revelatory fashion. "It was not till I was thirty years of age, till my experience was matured and condensed, till the flash of an intense illumination had thrown a fresh light upon it, that I was capable of understanding all the bearings of the phenomena which

---

*Later, when describing Louis' feverish anticipation of a union with the woman he loves, Balzac gives us another rupture with the world, this time the final one.

I witnessed at that early time." The description of Louis' struggle to preserve a semblance of order, to respond to the petty routine of the institution, to show interest in his studies, or even fear or respect when threatened with punishment, is a remarkable transcription of Balzac's own struggle with chaos, discipline and convention. It is a description of the innate maladaptation of the man of genius, of his blindness and deafness to everything except what he intuitively knows will nourish him. It is a picture of the anarchist who is later to become a martyr, or a tyrant, a portrait of the Will pure and naked. Even that irritating reproach which he puts in the mouth of the headmaster, the phrase which is forever startling Louis from his reveries, is significant since it is the tacit reproach which the world in its hatred and envy of the man of genius always makes: *"You are doing nothing!"* Balzac takes pains to make it clear that whenever Louis was accused of doing nothing he was probably most active in his own right way. It was from these seeming spells of inertia that Balzac's brilliant and devastating ideas were born. Subsequently, in expanding on Louis' philosophical speculations, he elucidates this cogently. There are two beings in us, he says—the Inner one, the Being of Action, and the External one, the Being of Reaction. The whole philosophy of duality enunciated through Louis Lambert is an effort on the part of Balzac, the artist, to establish a totality or acceptance of life. It is Balzac's own dynamic, positive interpretation of what we know as Tao. It runs counter to the whole European trend of metaphysics, which is purely intellectual and idealistic, and ends in a cul de sac.

At any rate, it was the "Poet-and-Pythagoras," as he styles his twin self, who was crushed by the educational routine, "as gold is crushed into round coin under the press." They were an idle and incorrigible pair who could neither play ball, nor run races, nor walk on stilts. "Aliens from the pleasures enjoyed by the others, we were outcasts, sitting forlorn under a tree in the playing-ground." "The eagle that needed the world to feed him," he adds, "was shut up between four narrow dirty walls. And thus Louis Lambert's life became 'an *ideal* life' in the strictest meaning of the words."

At eighteen, having lost his parents, Louis leaves college. He makes his home with his uncle who, having been turned out of his benefice, had come to settle at Blois. There Louis lives for some time, but consumed by a desire to complete his studies, he goes to Paris "to drink of science at its highest fount." The few thousand francs which he had inherited vanish during his three years in Paris. At the age of twenty-three he returns to Blois, driven out "by sufferings to which the impecunious are exposed there." In a long letter to his uncle, written at intervals during his sojourn in Paris, Louis pours out his impressions and experiences. It is no doubt a transcript of Balzac's own experiences upon first coming to Paris. Back in Blois, at the first house to which he is introduced by his uncle, Louis meets a Mademoiselle Pauline de Villenoix, a young and beautiful Jewess, the richest heiress in Blois. Louis falls madly in love with her at first sight. Three years after Louis' return to Blois Balzac encounters the aged uncle in the diligence, while on his way to that town, and through him learns that Louis, on the eve of his announced wedding to Mademoiselle de Villenoix, had gone mad. The uncle, who had taken Louis to Paris to be examined by the eminent physicians of that city, was informed that the malady was incurable. The physicians had advised that Louis "be left in perfect solitude, and that he should always live in a cool room with a subdued light." His fiancée insists on devoting herself to him nevertheless. She removes him to her château at Villenoix, where Balzac, two years later, arrives to visit them. Louis does not recognize his old chum, and after a prolonged effort to get him to break the silence, the only words he utters are—"the angels are white." Before leaving, Balzac obtains from Louis' devoted companion a few fragments of his thoughts (given as an appendix) which she had written down. Louis Lambert dies at the age of twenty-eight in his true love's arms.

The cornerstone of Louis Lambert's philosophy, by which he explained everything, was his theory of the angels. This theory, which Balzac borrowed from Swedenborg, is worth giving in its entirety, for it is this view of man which Balzac later raises to apotheosis in *Seraphita*. It is the highest expression of the duality which he sensed in his own nature and which he transmuted through art. . . .

"In each of us there are two distinct beings. According to Swedenborg, the angel is an individual in whom the inner being conquers the external being. If a man desires to earn his call to be an angel, as soon as his mind reveals to him his twofold existence, he must strive to foster the delicate angelic essence that exists within him. If, for lack of a lucid apprehension of his destiny, he allows bodily action to predominate, instead of confirming his intellectual being, all his powers will be absorbed in the use of his external senses, and the angel will slowly perish by the materialization of both natures. [Which is precisely what happened to Balzac!] In the contrary case, if he nourishes his inner being with the aliment needful to it, the soul triumphs over matter and strives to get free. [In this Louis Lambert failed, but Seraphita succeeded!]

"When they separate by the act of what we call death, the angel, strong enough then to cast off its wrappings, survives and begins its real life. The infinite variety which differentiates individual men can only be explained by this twofold existence which, again, is proved and made intelligible by that variety.

"In point of fact, the wide distance between a man whose torpid intelligence condemns him to evident stupidity, and one who, by the exercise of his inner life, has acquired the gift of some power, allows us to suppose that there is as great a difference between men of genius and other beings as there is between the blind and those who see. This hypothesis, since it extends creation beyond all limits, gives us, as it were, the clue to heaven. The beings who, here on earth, are apparently mingled without distinction, are there distributed, according to their inner perfection, in distinct spheres whose speech and manners have nothing in common. In the invisible world, as in the real world, if some native of the lower spheres comes, all unworthy, into a higher sphere, not only can he never understand the customs and languages there, but his mere presence paralyzes the voice and hearts of those who dwell therein."

Here, embedded in the midst of a work which was only too obviously destined to be neglected by the great majority of his admirers, Balzac, like one of those medieval masons at work on a cathedral, leaves the visible evidence of his secret initiation into the mysteries. In the very next breath, as though to give the clue to the high importance of this passage, he mentions Dante's *Divine Comedy*, which is the mystic cathedral of words that enshrines the great Rosicrucian mystery of the Middle Ages. But why he should have said that "Dante had perhaps some slight intuition of those spheres which begin in the world of torment and rise circle on circle, to the highest heaven," baffles me. Why "slight" intuition? Was he appalled by Dante's audacity? Had he too recently fallen under the dominion of the "Buddha of the North," as he styles Swedenborg? He was no doubt highly familiar with Dante's work. In *The Exiles,* the last of the three studies which make up *Le Livre Mystique,* he records an episode in Dante's life which occurred during his stay in Paris whilst attending the celebrated Sigier, "the most noted doctor of Mystical Theology of the University of Paris." But possibly the real clue to this apparent "slight" is given in what follows upon the theory of the angels, viz., the *role of love.* To Lambert, says Balzac, "pure love—love as we dream of it in youth—was the coalescence of two angelic natures. Nothing could exceed the fervency with which he longed to meet a woman angel. And who better than he could inspire or feel love?" Strangely enough, though Louis Lambert is destined to meet and to be loved by precisely the angelic creature he sought in his dreams, the union is tragically aborted and Louis is robbed of the fruits of his yearning. The interval which marks the short separation in time between the appearance of *Louis Lambert* and *Seraphita* is not the merely natural one attributed to artistic ripening, but rather it seems to me, a time difference (of infinite duration or brevity) as between one incarnation and another. As a human being, Louis Lambert had not earned the right to be wedded to an angel in the flesh. His madness, which breaks out on the eve of the wedding, seems at first more like the voluntary assumption of a Purgatorial role, in preparation for the higher union which is to take place when Louis, reincarnated as Seraphita-Seraphitus, elects to espouse Heaven. "The fortuitous separation of our two natures," which is one of the phrases Balzac employs in describing Louis' pathologic condition, is an occurrence familiar to Hindus and Tibetans, and the causes ascribed by them differ considerably from the scientific explanations offered us by the psychopathologist. The cataleptic states which signalled Louis' sudden swerve from "pure idealism to the most intense sensualism" were as familiar to Balzac as the epileptic attacks described by Dostoievski. "The excitement to which he had been wound up by the anticipation of acute physical enjoyment, enhanced by a chaste life and a highly-strung soul, had no doubt led to these attacks, of which the results are as little known as the cause," says Balzac. "What was really extraordinary," he comments significantly, "is that Louis should not have had several previous attacks, since his habits of rapt thought and the character of his mind would predispose him to them." This, of course, Balzac is able to say without fear of refutation because he is speaking from intimate experience. The walking somnambulist who was returned to his parents at the age of fourteen was well qualified to speak on the relation between ecstasy and catalepsy. Says Louis Lambert: "Deep meditation and rapt ecstasy are perhaps the undeveloped germs of catalepsy." This in the course of a discussion of their favorite subject, for as Balzac writes, the two of them "went crazy over catalepsy."

However, what *is* truly extraordinary, in my opinion, is that Balzac himself did not succumb to madness. The study of Louis Lambert's morbid degeneration is really the story of Balzac's own narrow escape. Endowed with extraordinary vitality, he succeeded somehow in holding on to reason by that one invisible, indestructible hair. But by all the logic of fate and circumstance he should have perished like his double. It is the classic fate of the genius in modern times. Deprived of the maternal affection which a sensitive, precocious child demands, incarcerated like a leper in the educational penitentiary of the College of Vendôme, his unusual gifts unrecognized by his educators, condemned to the tower for long periods, like a convict, having no one to commune with but his imaginary double, experiencing all the terrors of schizophrenia, the miracle is that Balzac survived the ordeal even as well as he did. The story has a triple significance. In the ordinary child the result would be insanity, or psychosis; in the budding genius the result is a transmutation of suffering permitting us a work of art (I refer to his complete works) which is typical only of the art of the Western world, that is to say, an art which is at once a tribute to the imperishable angel in man and a prophecy of the fate which lies in store for a people whose culture is founded on the persecution and suppression of the highest types. With Louis Lambert there perished a seer; only the artist survived, in the person of Balzac. But the loss is irreparable. Not even the discovery of a companion, another angelic creature like himself, could preserve the better half of Balzac from dying. Towards the end of the book, when he is discussing Louis' case with the aged uncle, he chooses his words most carefully. Was not Louis' malady, he asks, perhaps the result of possessing a too highly organized nature? "If," he says, "he is really a victim of the malady as yet unstudied in all its aspects, which is known simply as madness, I am inclined to attribute it to his passion. His studies and his mode of life had strung his powers and faculties to a degree of energy beyond which the least further strain was too much for nature; Love was enough to crack them, or to raise them to a new form of expression which we are maligning perhaps, by ticketing it without due knowledge. In fact, he may perhaps have regarded the joys of marriage as an obstacle to the perfection of his inner man and his flight towards spiritual spheres."

Knowing Balzac's life as we do, are we not to infer that this desire for perfection, coupled with an uncontrollable passion, prevented him from realizing the joys of marriage? The truth is that it was desire at war with itself which frustrated Balzac. Louis, though chaste, succumbs to his sensual nature. Balzac, also capable of great chastity, succumbs to his inordinate passion for power and recognition. Whereas Louis Lambert succumbs to the devil, as it were, by ignoring the physical part of his being, Seraphita, who, as I hinted before, might be regarded as the subsequent incarnation of this strange being, triumphs over the demons in every Shape and Species! Seraphita *knows* evil; Louis is ignorant of it. Louis Lambert evinces neither lust nor

hatred—at the most, an indignant, silent scorn for his persecutors. With Dante, to take a familiar example, we trav-
erse every region of Hell, are confronted with every form
of evil. It is the audacious and sane solution later pro-
pounded through the poetic genius of Blake. It is acceptance, total acceptance, of every phase of life. Only thus
is there, or can there be, any spiral evolution, involution,
or devolution possible. The path is the same for God as
for man, the same for the vegetable as for the star. Balzac
never fully accepted life; he struggled, as we know from
the endless stories about him, first against sleep, the restor-
ative agency, second against death, the mystery which he
longed to embrace. Crucified by passion and desire, he
represents, like Beethoven, the very incarnation of a restless, tortured spirit. In his living he denied his own philosophy: he split and foundered on the antagonism of his own
being. Of Louis Lambert he says that the latter had even
reached the point of "preparing to perform on himself the
operation to which Origen believed he owed his talents."
It is only when Balzac perceives the deep meaning of cas-
tration, when he realizes the real nature of his conflict, that
he is able to conceive of a creature more evolved, a being
burned by the fires of temptation, the one he calls Seraphita, in whom the male and female halves of our being
are truly wedded, one in whom good and evil are so balanced that the real transition into a higher state of being
is made possible. In this lofty conception of the essential
nature of man Balzac leaps forward to a realization which
it may yet require thousands of years to justify but which
is undeniably true and inevitable. Like Dostoievski, Balzac
discerned the coming of a dawn in which the very essence
of man's nature would be profoundly altered; Lawrence
had a similar vision when he proclaimed the advent of
the era of the Holy Ghost. It is an idea which astrologers
associate with the Aquarian Age which, according to some,
we entered about the time of Balzac's birth, which again
is coincident with the time in which the story of *Seraphita*
is laid. *"Outside,"* he says, at the conclusion of that book,
"the first summer of the new century was in all its glory."
But *inside* the seed was blossoming into life—the seed of
that future which now seems so black, but wherein man

will find salvation through his own efforts. The whole emphasis with Lawrence, Dostoievski and Balzac, is on the *creative* powers of man. In them, in their vision of the world to come, the Christ spirit is seen to be triumphant. The Saviour is dead, they seem to cry, *long live the Saviours!* And the saviours of man, as every creative spirit knows, is man.

It is worth noting here the comparison which Spengler makes between Dostoievski and Tolstoi. "Dostoievski is a saint," says he, "Tolstoi only a revolutionary. To Dostoievski's Christianity the next thousand years will belong. . . . Tolstoi is the former Russia, Dostoievski the coming Russia. He [Dostoievski] has passed beyond both Petrinism and revolution, and from *his* future he looks back over them as from afar. His soul is apocalyptic, yearning, desperate, but of his future *certain*. . . . 'Conservative' and 'revolutionary' were terms of the West that left him indifferent. Such a soul as his can look beyond everything that we call social, for the things of this world seem to it so unimportant as not to be worth improving. No genuine religion aims at improving the world of facts, and Dostoievski, like every primitive Russian, is fundamentally unaware of that world and lives in a second, metaphysical world beyond."

What is the final expression of humanity, according to Balzac? In *Seraphita* he expresses it thus: "The union of love with a spirit of wisdom lifts the creature into the divine state in which the soul is woman and the body man." This is the final expression of humanity, "in which the spirit is supreme over the form."

In the case of Louis Lambert the spring of passion is muddied at the source. The conflict in his nature, repressed for so long, bursts out at the most unexpected moment, when, as I have said, he is about to ally himself to the angelic creature of his choice. Did we not know the events of Balzac's own life the tragedy would seem less convincing. When I express the opinion that Balzac was miraculously spared the fate of his double, I am only saying what Balzac himself implies throughout and what he seems to attest in dedicating his *Seraphita* to Madame Hanska. At the very threshold of maturity he had found a mother and a mistress in the person of Madame de Berny; he had other loves too, but in none, as he admits, could he find the companionship, the sympathy and the understanding which he demanded of a woman. He was not to find it in Madame Hanska either, for that matter, but because of his great passion for her he was given to find the solution within himself, a solution, be it said, sufficient to carry on, to plunge himself in work, to adapt himself to the world by creating his own world. The *partial* solution of the artist! Balzac was aware that it was only a partial solution, and reconciled himself to it. Never able to reach the center of his being, he at any rate succeeded in situating himself at a point whence he glimpsed the angel of creation. In *Louis Lambert* this parallax, or angle of displacement, becomes enormous, because Louis is moved nearer to the point of fixation. Louis' whole desire is fixed on the beyond—obstinately fixed, one might almost say. Louis' desire to commune with the angels, perhaps just because it is inflexible and unswerving, entrains a dénouement which is in perfect accordance with the law of consequence: Louis remains fixed and his wings are burned in the blinding light that invades him. Louis' madness *is* like Nijinsky's, of an exceptional character. If he be a lunatic, he is an extraordinary lunatic! Balzac, be it noted, took pains to portray him as a higher type of man whose motives are pure, whose intelligence is vast. But it is wisdom which Louis lacks, the wisdom of life, which come from experience. In the *Book of the Golden Precepts* it is written: "Learn above all to separate Head-learning from Soul-wisdom, the Eye from the Heart doctrine. Yea, ignorance is like unto a closed airless vessel; the soul a bird shut up within. It warbles not, nor can it stir a feather; but the songster mute and torpid sits, and of exhaustion dies." Louis' malady was diagnosed and minutely described thousands of years ago; today it is the universal malady. Despite the frenzied activity of the nations of the earth, *the songster mute and torpid sits and of exhaustion dies!*

Nobody knew better than Balzac that it is the wisdom of the heart which must prevail. He says it over and over again, in brilliant fashion. It is the heart of man which will rule in the ages to come, of that he is certain. But the heart must first be purified! and Louis Lambert, who had never *lived,* was inevitably destroyed by the very anticipation of a passionate release. "The selfish devotee lives to no purpose. The man who does not go through his appointed work in life has lived in vain. . . . In separation thou becomest the playground of Samvritti, origin of all the world's delusions."* The condition which Balzac is loath to call "madness" is really the demonic state of the world, which now horrifies us, and which is really the product of idealism. No century in history can boast of so many madmen, among its superior types, as the one following upon Balzac's time. The virulence of widespread disease, which we now recognize as schizophrenia, or to use a vulgar, literal expression—"soul-splitting"—is by no means a new phenomenon in the evolution of man's psychic being. It was known to the ancients also; it has been described again and again in occult lore; it is familiar to the saint and to the mystic. It might even be regarded as a beneficent punishment, inflicted upon the highest types among us in order to encourage a wider and deeper exploration of reality. Nothing more vividly resembles what we call "death" than the condition of neurosis. "He who isolates himself," says Eliphas Levi, "is given over to death thereby, and an eternity of isolation would be eternal death." No man, however, can give himself over to eternal death! But there is a living death, of which all occultists speak and of which even the most ordinary man has an understanding. In the highest sense, this is not a state to fear or avoid; it is a transitional state, containing promise or doom, according to the way we regard it. It is the moment, brief as a lightning flash or prolonged for a lifetime, in which, confronted by the necessity of a break with the past, we are paralyzed. It is the moment of arrest at the frontier of a new and greater realm of being. The majority of men, unable to seize the import of this new state or condition of mind, relapse, sink, founder and are carried off by the time current. The forward spirits accept the challenge and, even though they perish, remain with us in spirit to fecundate the new form of life.

In the person of Louis Lambert Balzac gives expression to the great paralyzing fear which beset him when con-

* (*Book of the Golden Precepts*)

fronted with the sublime duty which his nature had prepared him to obey. His vision, temporarily deflected, shed
a fantastic brilliance on the dream world in which he was
imprisoned. Louis is made to gaze steadfastly upon the
beyond, but with dead orbs. His sight is turned inward. He
remains fixed in the hallucinatory state of dream. As the
writer, Balzac liberated himself to swim in the ocean of the
universal imagination. Only by a miracle was he saved. But
he lost his soul! In this realm of the universal imagination,
to quote again from Eliphas Levi, we have "the source of
all apparitions, all extraordinary visions, and all the intuitive phenomena peculiar to madness or ecstasy. . . . Our
brain is a book printed within and without, and with the
smallest degree of excitement, the writing becomes blurred,
as occurs continually in cases of intoxication and madness.
*Dream then triumphs over real life and plunges reason in a
sleep which knows no waking. . . ."*

In the esoteric doctrine there is no "place" which corresponds to our conception of Hell; *"Avitchi,"* the Buddhist
equivalent to our Hell, is a state or condition, not a locality.
And, according to this doctrine, the greatest of all Hells is
Myalba, our earth. It is from a firsthand knowledge of this
Hell that Balzac wrote his books. When he parts company
with Louis at school he is parting company with the angel
he had endeavored to nourish. He sees nothing more of
Louis, nor does he hear of him again, until the accidental
meeting with Louis' uncle on his way to Blois. The account
of his struggles, his deceptions and disillusionment, as he
gives it to us in the long letter from Paris, is a description of
the torments of Hell. From this ordeal of fire Balzac
emerged only partially purified: he never fully accepted the
wisdom of the supreme test. His colossal activity as a man
of letters is only the reverse of the mute torpor in which
his double sits, or stands, without stirring a feather. Torpor
and activity are the two faces of the same malady: *action*
proceeds only from a being whose center is at rest. For
Balzac, as for the whole modern world, dream triumphed
over reason; the dreamer dies of exhaustion in his feverish
sleep of meaningless activity. He wrote in a world of the
imagination, but he lived in a world of things, amidst a
nightmare of bric-a-brac.

When, in *Seraphita,* rhapsodizing on Swedenborg's theory of the angels, Balzac appears to be struck by the expression "there are *solitary* angels," one feels that he has given this phrase his own special emphasis. This is further enhanced when, shortly afterwards, he remarks: "According to Swedenborg, God did not create angels independently; there are none but those who have been human beings on earth. Thus the earth is the nursery ground for heaven. The angels are not angels by original nature; they are transformed into angels by an intimate union with God which God never refuses, the very essence of God being never negative, but always active." One knows, that towards his thirtieth year Balzac finally caught a glimpse of the meaning of suffering, that as a writer he chose a path of renunciation which, though partial, enabled him to accept that Hell which a life on earth is for a man of genius. The ways of the earth had not changed, but Balzac himself had changed since that period of youth which he describes in *Louis Lambert.* By accepting the role of writer, bitter as it was, he was able to work out a partial solution of his lot. When, in the narrative, he comes back to Louis, as he promised he would one day, he finds the angelic being lost to the world. The single self which he had molded into an artist looks back upon the divided self which he formerly was. The angelic youth is swallowed up in dream and illusion; the warrior who battled the world and triumphed, after his fashion, discerns in his counterpart only the husk of his adolescent self. The man who would remain pure and undefiled is turned to clay; he is returned to the earth, to Hell, as it were, robbed of the light and splendor of the living soul. Rodin, in wrestling with the problem of immortalizing this conflict in stone, has given eloquent form and expression to the antagonism which lodged in Balzac with sphinx-like tenacity. In that rough-hewn mold of heavy earth, in which Balzac's soul was imprisoned, the Buddhist drama of Desire was played out in a manner such as we have never witnessed in another European.

The man to whom Balzac was tremendously indebted for an understanding of the World of Desire was Louis Claude Saint-Martin, *"le philosophe inconnu"* whose ideas, according to Curtius, he took over bodily. Balzac was this

"Homme de Désir" of whom Saint-Martin wrote. Saint-Martin's system of philosophy, derived from Martinez Pasquales' law of numbers, the revelations of Swedenborg and the visions of Jacob Boehme, is based essentially on the idea that man can always find his unity in himself. The following brief commentaries on his doctrine may serve to give an idea of the relation of Balzac's theories to Saint-Martin's philosophy. . . .

"For Saint-Martin man turned to another light than that for which he was destined to be the supreme manifestation, and matter was born out of the Fall; for God created matter to arrest man's precipitation into the abyss, and to give him a world where he would have a chance to redeem himself. In the actual state of things, man holds deep within him the vestiges of his first destiny and the obscure reminiscence of the Golden Age, the primitive paradise. If he comes to listen to the interior signs which are given him, and to descend within himself until he is able, by a spiritual magic, to grasp the germs which brood in his soul, he will achieve his own reintegration in God; but, at the same time, he will restore the entire Creation to its primordial Unity. Man alone, artisan of the Fall, can be the workman for reconciliation, the saviour of Nature. He is a being charged to continue God, there where God no longer is known by Himself alone. . . . He continues it in the series of manifestations and emanations, because *there* God is to be known by images and representatives.' If the man of desire craves for harmony and unity, it is because he holds in himself the vestiges, for one cannot crave what one has not first previously known. *'Everything tends to the unity from which it issued.'* The principal agent for this reintegration is the word, which holds the analogy with the Word which created the world; and that is why the act of the poet is sacred and literally creative. Music, in her turn, can contribute to this redeeming magic, since its principle, number, is the reflection of the numbers which rule the courses of the stars, the centuries and the whole of Nature."*

"The human soul, says Saint-Martin, is an extract of the 'universal divine.' " However, he makes it consist of one sole faculty, the will, which in turn he confounds in his

*From *"L'Ame Romantique et le Rêve"*—Albert Béguin.

mind with desire. But desire, for him, is the basis, the root of our being. It is through desire that "God first entered into us, and it is through desire that we have the power of returning to Him; for desire, being the result of the separation of the two existences which, because of the similarity of their natures, experience the need to be united, is necessarily in God as in man. The desire of man, as long as he is not corrupted, is the development of the divine properties that are in us, and the desire of God is the communication of his properties, is the infiltration of this marvellous sap without which man falls back on himself dry and withered. . . . This is why Saint-Martin defines man as the desire of God, and shows us, as the highest dignity to which we may aspire, that of *l'homme de désir*." *

Before proceeding to the "letter" which Louis Lambert pens to his uncle, and which is dated 1819, it may be worth while to observe that in a letter to Madame Hanska (1846) Balzac explains that he had never had a mother, that by the time he was eighteen his mother had rendered his life so miserable that he was obliged to leave home and install himself in a garret, in Paris (Rue Lesdiguières), where he led the life described in *La Peau de Chagrin*. It should also be borne in mind that when he announced his intention to abandon the law for literature his parents accorded him just one year in which to prove his ability as a writer. In this letter to Madame Hanska, wherein he speaks of his mother's hatred for himself and his sister, he says: "Laurence she killed, but I, I am alive." It is this period in Paris which, as he says in *Louis Lambert,* was to "close this portentous childhood and unappreciated youth." This letter, he says, "betrays the struggle of Louis' soul at the time when youth was ending and the terrible power of production was coming into being." And, as though to close the poignant cry of distress which is still fresh in his memory, he concludes: "Are there not some lofty souls who endeavor to concentrate their powers by long silence, so as to emerge fully capable of governing the world by word or by deed?"

The spectacle of "Parisian civilization" which presented itself to Louis Lambert's eyes is the picture of a world in

* *"Le Mysticisme Français du 18e Siècle"*—Adolphe Franck.

decay. The death and disintegration which Balzac sensed over a century ago has now seemingly reached its maximum. Today every great world-city stinks to high heaven, and it is from this death of the world that the artist is obliged to draw his inspiration. I give the gist of Louis' lamentation in telegraphic style. . . .

"I find no one here who likes what I like . . . or is amazed at what amazes me. Thrown back on myself, I eat my heart out in misery. . . . Here, money is the mainspring of everything, even for going without money. . . . I am not frightened at poverty. If it were not that beggars are imprisoned, branded, scorned, I would beg, to enable me to solve at my leisure the problems that haunt me. . . . Everything here checks the flight of a spirit that strives towards the future. I should not be afraid of myself in a desert cave; I am afraid of myself here. . . . Here man has a thousand wants which drag him down. You go out walking, absorbed in dreams; the voice of the beggar asking an alms brings you back to this world of hunger and thirst. You need money only to take a walk. . . . Your organs of sense, perpetually wearied by trifles, never get any rest. The poet's sensitive nerves are perpetually shocked, and what ought to be his glory becomes his torment; his imagination is his cruellest enemy . . . Even vice and crime here find a refuge and charity, but the world is merciless to the inventor, to the man who thinks. Here everything must show an immediate and practical result. . . . The State might pay talent as it pays the bayonet; but it is afraid of being taken in by mere cleverness, as if genius could be counterfeited for any length of time. . . . At the Museum a professor argues to prove that another in the Rue St. Jacques talks nonsense. . . . A professor of philosophy may make a name by explaining how Plato is Platonic. . . . Professors are appointed to produce simpletons—how else can we account for a scheme devoid of method or any notion of the future? . . . This vagueness and uncertainty prevails in politics as well as in science. . . . Politics, at the present time, place human forces in antagonism to neutralize each other, instead of combining them to promote their action to some definite end. . . . I see no fixed purpose in politics; its constant agitation has led to no progress. . . . The arts, which are the direct outcome of the individual, the products of genius or handicraft, have not advanced much. . . . Man is still the same: might is still his only law, and success his only wisdom. . . . No political theory has ever lasted. Governments pass away, as men do, without handing down any lesson, and no system gives birth to a system better than that which preceded it. . . . Means are lacking both for attack and for resistance. If we should be invaded, the people must be crushed; it has lost its mainspring—its leaders. The man who should foresee two centuries ahead would die on the place of execution. . . ."

And now let us contrast these bitter reflections on the state of France in the early 19th century with another picture of decay and corruption such as it presented itself to the eyes of a man in the so-called New World. The citation is from Walt Whitman's *Democratic Vistas* (1870), written shortly after the victory of the North in the Civil War. . . .

"Never was there, perhaps, more hollowness at heart than at present, and here in the United States. Genuine belief seems to have left us. The underlying principles of the United States are not honestly believed in . . . nor is humanity itself believed in. . . . The spectacle is appalling. We live in an atmosphere of hypocrisy throughout. . . . The depravity of the business classes of our country is not less than has been supposed, but infinitely greater. The official services of America, national, state and municipal, in all their branches and departments, except the judiciary, are saturated in corruption, bribery, falsehood, mal-administration; and the judiciary is tainted. The great cities reek with respectable as much as non-respectable robbery and scoundrelism. . . . The magician's serpent in the fable ate up all the other serpents; and money-making is our magician's serpent, remaining today sole master of the field. . . . I say that our New World democracy, however great a success in uplifting the masses out of their sloughs, in materialistic development, products, and in a certain highly-deceptive superficial popular intellectuality, is, so far, an almost complete failure in its social aspects, and in really grand religious, moral, literary and aesthetic results. . . . In vain have we annexed Texas, California, Alaska, and reach north for Canada and south for Cuba. It is as if we were somehow being endowed with a vast and more and more thoroughly appointed body, and then left with little or no soul. . . . Coming down to what is of the only real importance, Personalities, and examining minutely, we question, we ask, Are there, indeed, *men* here worthy the name? . . . Are there arts worthy of freedom and a rich people? Is there a grand moral and religious civilization—the only justification of a great material one? Confess that to severe eyes, using the moral microscope upon humanity, a sort of dry and flat Sahara appears, these cities, crowded with petty grotesques, malformations, phantoms, playing meaningless antics. Confess that everywhere, in shop, street, church, theatre, bar room, official chair, are pervading flippancy and vulgarity, low cunning, infidelity—everywhere the youth puny, impudent, foppish, prematurely ripe—everywhere an abnormal libidinousness, unhealthy forms, male, female, painted, padded, dyed, chignoned, muddy complexions, bad blood, the capacity for good motherhood decreasing or deceased, shallow notions of beauty, with a range of manners, or rather lack of manners (considering the advantages enjoyed), probably the meanest to be seen in the world."

Here are two diagnoses of modern society by men of vision and integrity. Both of them were vilified by the critics of the day; both of them waged an unholy struggle for recognition, Whitman even going so far as to peddle his book from door to door. Since their day the struggle of the creative individual has become increasingly difficult: it is a deadlock, between the man of genius and the mob. Practically all the governments of the world, since their time, have fallen; manners have not improved, nor art either, and as for faith and religiousness, it is even more absent than ever.

"Sooner or later," says Whitman, "we come down to one single, solitary soul. . . . In the future of these States must arise poets immenser far, *and make great poems of death.* The poems of life are great, but there must be the poems of the purport of life, not only in itself, but beyond itself. . . . Surely this universal ennui, this coward fear, this shuddering at death, these low, degrading views, are not always to rule the spirit pervading future society, as it has the past, and does the present. . . ." (Italics mine.)

And what is Balzac's conclusion, as we receive it through the utterances of Louis Lambert? After asking himself why he had come to Paris, why he was given such vast faculties without being permitted to use them, asking what meaning to give his sufferings if he is to suffer unknown, he says: "Just as that blossom vainly sheds its fragrance to the solitude, so do I, here in a garret, give birth to ideas that no one can grasp. . . . My point is to ascertain the real relation that may exist between God and man. Is not this a need of the age? . . . If man is bound up with everything, is there not something above him with which he again is bound up? If he is the end-all of the unexplained transmutations that lead up to him, must he not be also the link between the visible and invisible creations? The activity of the universe is not absurd; it must tend to an end, and that end is surely not a social body constituted as ours is! . . . It seems to me that we are on the eve of a great human struggle; the forces are there, only I do not see the General. . . . I feel in myself a life so luminous that it might enlighten a world, and yet I am shut up in a sort of mineral. . . . I should need to embrace the whole world, to clasp and re-create it; but those who have done this, who have embraced and remoulded it, began—did they not?—by being a wheel in the machine. *I can only be crushed.*" (Italics mine.)

The core of Louis Lambert's philosophy may be said to be the idea of unity in duality. Balzac's whole life and work, as Curtius well says, represent a veritable "search for the absolute." The sustained antagonism in the very heart and core of life is the key-note; it is the same passionate quest, the same struggle to wrest from life the secret of creation, which influenced D. H. Lawrence in writing *The Crown.* "For Balzac," to quote Curtius again, "unity is a mystic principle, the mark, the seal of the Absolute." In the book called *The Search for the Absolute* this secret of the philosopher's stone is discovered by the hero only when he is dying.

Louis Lambert's views may be briefly summarized thus. . . . All life reflects the antagonism between inner and outer, will and thought, spirit and feeling. Man is a dual being, expressing the rhythm of the universe in action and reaction. At the basis of all life is one etheric substance, manifestation of a primal energy, assuming infinite forms of manifestation and evidencing itself to our senses as matter. In man this primordial substance is transformed into psychic energy, or will. The special attribute of this will is thought, whose organs are the five senses which, in reality, are but differentiations of one sense, *vision*. Vision expresses itself through the mysterious phenomenon of the Word. Everything in the universe is indicative of an hierarchical order. Over and above the three realms of nature is the world of ideas. Ideas are living creatures, active and activating, like flowers. This world of ideas may be divided into three spheres: instinct, abstraction and specialism. The majority of men are prisoners of instinct; a small number attain to the level of abstraction, with the emergence of which society may be said to begin. It is from this level that laws, the arts and all social creations emerge. Specialism is the gift of intuition which permits man to see the inner as well as the outer in all its ramifications. (The perfection of the inner eye gives rise to the gift of Specialism.) The human genius is a type functioning in a realm between abstraction and intuition. Intuition, consequently, is the most satisfactory and adequate form, the highest form of knowing. To know is to *see*. There is at bottom only one science, and all the imperfect forms of knowledge are nothing but a confused vision! This "superior science," which Louis Lambert proclaims, is what Balzac styles *"le magisme,"* a term not to be confused with magic or Magianism. (Already, in 1847, Balzac was dreaming of the establishment by the Sorbonne of a new school of "occult philosophy," under the name of Anthropology. This dream was subsequently to be realized, under the name of Anthroposophy, by Rudolph Steiner.)

In the fragments of Louis Lambert's "system," recorded by his faithful companion, Mademoiselle de Villenoix, which come as a sort of appendix to the story, these ideas are put down in the form of aphoristic notes. In apologizing for the cryptic, fragmentary quality of these speculations, Balzac says: "I ought perhaps to have made a separate book of these fragments of thought, intelligible only to certain spirits who have been accustomed to lean over the edge of abysses in the hope of seeing to the bottom. The life of that mighty brain, which split up on every side, like a too vast empire, would have been set forth in the narrative of this man's visions—a being incomplete for lack of force or of weakness; but I preferred to give an account of my own impressions rather than to compose a more or less poetical romance." As a matter of fact, earlier in the book, Balzac gives us the clue to the terminology employed in the Aphorisms. "New ideas," he says, "require new words, or a new and expanded use of older words, extended and defined in their meaning." Thus Lambert, to set forth the basis of his system, had adopted certain common words that answered to his notions. The word *Will* he used to connote the medium in which the mind moves, or to use a less abstract expression, the mass of power by which man can reproduce, outside himself, the actions constituting his external life. *Volition*—a word due to Locke—expressed the act by which a man exerts his will. The word *Mind,* or *Thought,* which he regarded as the quintessential product of the Will, also represented the medium in which the ideas originate and to which thought gives substance. The *Idea,* a name common to every creation of the brain, constituted the act by which man uses his mind. Thus the Will and the Mind were two generating forces; the Volition and the Idea were the two products. . . . According to him, the Mind and Ideas are the motion and the outcome of our inner organization, just as the Will and Volition are of our external activity. He gave the Will precedence over the Mind. *You must will before you can think,* he said.

To Louis Lambert, *Will* and *Thought* were living forces, as Balzac says. "The elements of Will and Mind," says Louis Lambert, "may perhaps be found; but there will always remain beyond apprehension the x against which I once used to struggle. That x is the Word, the Logos. . . . From your bed to the frontiers of the universe there are but two steps: Will and Faith. . . . Facts are nothing; they do not subsist; all that lives of us is the Idea." He points out that Jesus possessed the gift of Specialism. "He saw each fact in its root and in its results, in the past whence it had its rise, and in the future where it would grow and spread. . . ."

According to Balzac, Louis Lambert had too much good sense to dwell among the clouds of theories. "He had sought for proofs of his theories in the history of great men, whose lives, as set forth by their biographers, supply very curious particulars as to the operation of the understanding." The description of Louis which he gives at the time of their parting is altogether that of a man preparing to lead the life of an initiate. "He ate little and drank water only; either by instinct or by choice he was averse to any exertion that made a demand on his strength; his movements were few and simple, like those of Orientals or of savages, with whom gravity seems a condition of nature. Though naturally religious, Louis did not accept the minute practices of the Roman ritual; his ideas were more intimately in sympathy with Saint Theresa and Fénelon, and several Fathers and certain Saints who, in our day, would be regarded as heresiarchs or atheists. . . . To him Jesus Christ was the most perfect type of his system. *Et Verbum caro factum est* seemed a sublime statement intended to express the traditional formula of the Will, the Word and the Act made visible. Christ's consciousness of His Death—having so perfected His inner Being by divine works, that one day the invisible form of it appeared to His disciples—and the other Mysteries of the Gospels, the magnetic cures wrought by Christ, and the gifts of tongues, all to him confirmed his doctrine. . . . He discerned the strongest evidence of his theory in most of the martyrdoms endured during the first century of our era, which he spoke of as the great era of the *Mind*."

There is one more passage, in this connection, which seems to me worthy of attention. After referring to Louis Lambert's study of the laws of Mind and Will, and their correlations, Balzac says: "Louis Lambert had accounted for a multitude of phenomena which, till then, had been regarded with reason as incomprehensible. Thus wizards, men possessed, those gifted with second sight, and demoniacs of every degree—the victims of the Middle Ages —became the subject of explanations so natural, that their very simplicity often seemed to me the seal of their truth.

The marvellous gifts which the Church of Rome, jealous of all mysteries, punished with the stake, were, in Louis' opinion, the result of certain affinities between the constituent elements of matter and those of mind, which proceed from the same source."

The triumph of energy, will and faith in man, the existence of magic and the evidences of the miraculous, the relation of God to man through Desire, the notion of hierarchies in every realm of life, as well as the belief in transmutation, all these manifestations of the spiritual attributes of man, Balzac has summed up in the story of his own life, or rather of the most important years of his life, the period of germination. The period, in other words, *when the terrible powers of production were coming into being.*

In the Rue Cassini, where he wrote so many of his great works, Balzac is reported to have said to George Sand: "Literature! but my dear lady, literature doesn't exist! There is life, of which politics and art are part. I am a man who's alive, that's all . . . a man living his life, nothing more." Whereupon he proceeded to forfeit his life through the bondage of work. He wanted to be great ("man must be great or not be at all," are his words), and he *was* great, but he died a failure. Perhaps the best justification of his failure is the one he makes himself somewhere. "The man of genius," he said, "is one who can invariably convert his thoughts into deeds. But the truly outstanding genius does not unremittingly allow this evolution to take place; if he did, he would be the equal of God."

At the best, it is a poor excuse. Balzac, like Beethoven, seemingly gave the maximum that a man can give, but it was not enough, *not for a Balzac!* I am not thinking of the forty books he is said to have left unfinished at his death, but of the life he left unlived, of the vision he failed to live by. His life, which is the very symbol of Work, epitomizes the futility of Western life, with its emphasis on doing rather than being; it epitomizes the sterility of even the highest efforts when characterized, as they are in our world, by the divorce between action and belief.

If Louis Lambert's life may be regarded as a typical example of the crucifixion of genius by the society in which he was born, Balzac's own life may be regarded as a typical example of the immolation exacted of our superior types through a limited conception of, and a slavish devotion to, art. The criticism of the social structure which Balzac makes, not only in this book but in all his books, is absolutely just. But it is only half the picture. There is a duty which devolves upon every individual, regardless of the state of society into which he is born. Art is only the stepping-stone to another, larger way of life. If the artist himself is not converted by the Word, what hope can there be for the masses who read him? It is not enough to lead the life of an inspired drudge; will and faith, activated by desire, should carry a man beyond such a mode of life. I have no respect for Balzac's herculean labors, nor for his colossal output, nor for his genius, when I realize that his life sputtered out ingloriously. If a man cannot find salvation in himself all his words are futile. The real Balzac died in the mythical person of Louis Lambert whose very name he tells us he disliked.

If the foregoing seems like a contradiction to all that I have written hitherto in this essay I am willing to let it remain a contradiction, for it is this contradiction which must be resolved, and especially by the artist. I cannot conclude without expressing my deep appreciation of Ernst-Robert Curtius' book, *Balzac,* from which I have liberally drawn both inspiration and material. This book, which is the most penetrating and comprehensive study of Balzac that I know of, has not enjoyed a great success in France. As in Balzac's own day, it seems probable that his greatest admirers continue to be foreigners. The canonization and immortalization of the dead, which seems to be the chief characteristic of French culture, has not, despite all the museum work, succeeded in revealing the full measure of Balzac's genius. The qualities of his mind which were most important the French still pretend to ignore, if not to deprecate and depreciate. The dead are still more honored than the living, and even the dead sometimes fail to receive their due. Nothing is changed since Louis Lambert's day. Perhaps no other people in the world, occupying the high cultural position which the French do, have mistreated and ignored their men of genius so persistently—unless it be the Greeks whom the French pretend to emulate. The mummification of ideas goes on as before, the forward spirits are crushed, the people, when they have a leader, are delivered over to death. Realism has taken the place of reality, and the true leaders are only discovered after their death.

■■

THE STAFF OF LIFE

BREAD: PRIME SYMBOL. Try and find a good loaf. You can travel fifty thousand miles in America without once tasting a piece of good bread. Americans don't care about good bread. They are dying of inanition but they go on eating bread without substance, bread without flavor, bread without vitamins, bread without life. Why? Because the very core of life is contaminated. If they knew what good bread was they would not have such wonderful machines on which they lavish all their time, energy and affection. A plate of false teeth means much more to an American than a loaf of good bread. Here is the sequence: poor bread, bad teeth, indigestion, constipation, halitosis, sexual starvation, disease and accidents, the operating table, artificial limbs, spectacles, baldness, kidney and bladder trouble, neurosis, psychosis, schizophrenia, war and famine. Start with the American loaf of bread so beautifully wrapped in cellophane and you end on the scrap heap at forty-five. The only place to find a good loaf of bread is in the ghettos. Wherever there is a foreign quarter there is apt to be good bread. Wherever there is a Jewish grocer or delicatessen you are almost certain to find an excellent loaf of bread. The dark Russian bread, light in weight, found only rarely on this huge continent, is the best bread of all. No vitamins have been injected into it by laboratory specialists in conformance with the latest food regulations. The Russian just naturally likes good bread, because he also likes caviar and vodka and other good things. Ameri-

71

cans are whiskey, gin and beer drinkers who long ago lost their taste for food. And losing that they have also lost their taste for life. For enjoyment. For good conversation. For everything worth while, to put it briefly.

What do I find wrong with America? Everything. I begin at the beginning, with the staff of life: bread. If the bread is bad the whole life is bad. Bad? Rotten, I should say. Like that piece of bread only twenty-four hours old which is good for nothing except perhaps to fill up a hole. Good for target practice maybe. Or shuttlecock and duffle board. Even soaked in urine it is unpalatable; even perverts shun it. Yet millions are wasted advertising it. Who are the men engaged in this wasteful pursuit? Drunkards and failures for the most part. Men who have prostituted their talents in order to help further the decay and dissolution of our once glorious Republic.

Here is one of the latest widely advertised products: Hollywood Bread. On the red, white and blue cellophane jacket in which it is wrapped, this last word in bread from the American bakeries, it reads as follows:

BAKED WITH

whole wheat flour, clear wheat flour, water, non-diastatic malt, yeast, salt, honey, caramel, whole rye flour, yeast food, stone ground oatmeal, soya flour, gluten flour, barley flour, sesame seed, and a small quantity of dehydrated (water free) vegetables including celery, lettuce, pumpkin, cabbage, carrots, spinach, parsley, sea kelp, added for flavor only.

The only thing missing from this concoction is powdered diamonds. How does it taste? Much like any other American product. Of course, this is a reducing bread of which one should eat two slices a day three times a day and not ask how it tastes. Grow thin, as in Hollywood, and be thankful it doesn't taste worse. That's the idea. For several days now I have been trying to get a whiff of some of those ingredients—sea kelp especially—which were included "for flavor only." Why they were not added for health too I don't know. Naturally all these delicious-sounding items amount to about one ten-thousandth part of the loaf. And on the second day, stale, flat and unprofitable, this marvelous new bread is no more attractive to the palate or the stomach than any other loaf of American bread. On the second day it is good for replacing a missing tile on the roof. Or to make a scratchboard for the cat.

The second day! If the first is given to creation, to light, let us say, the second (in America) is given up to garbage. Every second day is garbage day in America. I know because I have had lots to do with garbage. I've hauled it, for pay, and I've eaten it upon necessity. I learned to distinguish between one kind of bread and another by salvaging dry crusts from the garbage can. I don't know which is worse—the day of creation, when everything turns to gas and bilge, with its concomitants dandruff, constipation, halitosis, false teeth, artificial limbs, psychic impotency, and so on, or the second day, given up to garbage, when all creation turns out to be nothing but a mirage and a disillusionment. It has been said, and I have no doubt it is true, that the garbage accumulated by one big American city would feed certain of the little countries of Europe handsomely. I know no quicker way to kill off the warring nations of Europe than to feed them our garbage. The pygmies might thrive on it, possibly even the Chinese coolie, who is supposed to thrive on anything, but I cannot see the Danes, the Swiss, the Swedes, the Greeks, the Albanians, or the Austrians thriving on it. No Sir. I would sooner feed them buzzards than the left-overs from the American table. Already, with our canned food products, our cold storage meat, our dehydrated vegetables, we have brought about a tremendous deterioration in these sturdy people of Europe. From these to the machine and thence to war is but a step. Then, famine, plague, pestilence, dung heaps. And monuments, of course. All sorts of monuments. Done by second or third rate artists.

The care and affection which once was bestowed on the human body now goes to the machines. The machines get the best food, the best attention. Machines are expensive; human lives are cheap. Never in the history of the world was life cheaper than it is to-day. (And no pyramids to show for it either.) How natural, then, that the staff of life should be utterly without value. I begin with bread and I shall end with bread. I say we make the foulest bread in all the world. We pass it off like fake diamonds. We advertise it and sterilize it and protect it from all the germs of life. We make a manure which we eat before we have had time to eliminate it. We not only have failed God, tricked Nature, debased Man, but we have cheated the birds of the air with our corrupt staff of life. Everytime I fling the stale bread over the cliff I beg forgiveness of the birds for offering them our American bread. Perhaps that is why they are not singing any more as they used to when I was a child. The birds are pining and drooping. It's not the war, for they have never participated in our carnages. It's the bread. The stale, flat, unprofitable bread of the second day. It shortens their wing-span, weakens their umbrella-ribs, reduces the scope of their swoop, blunts their beaks, deteriorates their vision, and finally—it kills their song! If you don't believe me, ask any ornithologist. It's a known fact. And how Americans love facts!

Another fact. . . . Food, when it is not enjoyed, kills. The best diet in the world is useless if the patient has no appetite, no gusto, no sensuality. On the whole, Americans eat without pleasure. They eat because the bell rings three times a day. (I omit mention of the clay eaters of the South and other poor whites who live on rats, snakes, and cow-dung.) They don't eat because they love food. To prove it you have only to shove a glass of whiskey before them. See which they reach for first! And now, with vitamins and all the other life-savers, food has become even less important. Why bother trying to squeeze a bit of life out of our worn-out products of the soil? Why pretend? Throw anything down the hatch to stop the gnawing and swallow a dozen vitamins. That way you'll make sure you've had your proper dose of the vital essentials. Should the vitamins fail, see a surgeon. From there to the sanitarium. And from there to the nut-house—or the dung heap. Be sure to get a Hollywood funeral. They're the loveliest, the duckiest, the most sanitary, the most inspiring. And no more ex-pensive than ordinary ground burial. You can, if you like, have your dear lost one propped up in a natural reclining position, her cheeks rouged, a cigarette to her lips, and a phonograph record talking to you just as she once talked to you in life. The most wonderful fake imaginable. Jolly, what? O death, where is thy sting? What's more, she can be kept that way for an unspeakably long period; the cigarette is guaranteed not to rot away before the lips or the buttocks. You can come back and have a second, a third, a twenty-fifth look at the beloved. Still smoking a cigarette. Or you can have her reading a book, the *Iliad,* say, or the *Bhagavad Gita*—something uplifting like that.

I remember when I used to be served a slice of home-made bread with butter and sugar smeared over it. Glorious days! That bread really had a taste. *Schmeckt gut, nicht-wahr? Yah! Sehr gut. Wunderbar. Ausgezeichnet.* With a piece of bread like that I used to sit and read *Pinocchio* or *Alice Through the Looking Glass* or Hans Christian Andersen or *The Heart of a Boy.* Mothers had time in those days to make good bread with their own hands, and still do the thousand and one things which motherhood demands of a woman. To-day they haven't time to do anything, and hardly a bloody mother in the bloody land knows how to bake a loaf of bread. Mother gets up early now to work in an office or a factory. She's busy doing nothing all day, which is to say—earning a living. Earning a living has nothing to do with living. It's the belt line to the grave, without a transfer or a stopover. A one-way passage via the frying pan and the cookerless cooker. A child is an accident—bad rubber goods or else too much drink and recklessness. Any way, it's there and it has to be fed. You don't bake bread for accidents, do you? And why bother to produce milk from the breast when the cows are working over-time for the dairy companies of America?

Day by day the morons, epileptics and schizoids multiply. By accident, like everything else. Nothing is planned in America except improvements. And all improvements are for the machine. When a plenum is reached war is declared. Then the machine really gets going. War is a Roman Holiday for the machine. Man becomes even less than nothing then. The machine is well fed. The food products become plastics and plastics are what make the world go round. Better to have a good steering wheel than a good stomach. In the old days an army advanced on its stomach; now it advances in tanks or spitfires or superfortresses. Civilians never advance. Civilians always rot and help make insurance companies richer.

But bread. . . . Let's not forget, it's bread we want—and children that are not accidents brought about by defective rubber or bathtub gin. How to get it? Bread, I mean. By putting a monkey wrench in the machine. By going backwards on all fours, like giraffes with broken necks. By praying for life now and not hereafter. By exercising freedom and not inventing four, five or six freedoms won by the slaughter and starvation of twenty or thirty millions. Begin today by baking your own bread. First of all you need a stove. A wood or coal stove. Not a gas range. Not an electric apparatus. Then let the flies in. Then roll your sleeves up and get your hands in the dough. Lick your fingers. Never mind if you lose your job. Eat your bread first, then maybe you won't want to work in an office or a factory. Life begins with bread. And a prayer. Not a begging prayer, but a prayer of thanks. Don't bless the block-busters. Bless God for his favors—air, water, sun, moon. God wants you to enjoy the bread of life. He never meant you to go out all day working at a job you loathe so that you can buy a loaf of store bread wrapped in cellophane. God gave us germs as well as air and water and sun. Germs attack only what is already rotting. Man is rotting in every fibre of his being: that is why he is a prey to germs. And that is why he is allergic to everything that is for his own good.

Before Communism was there was Communion and before that there was God and God said let there be light and there was light. And what a glorious light it was. It lasted for aeons, and then came the scientific age and darkness fell upon the land everywhere. Now everything can be proved backwards and out of existence and instead of soaring with our own wings or on the backs of our giant birds we make things of metal and plastics which spread havoc and destruction in their wake. We throw bones to the dogs and eat the dogs instead of the bones. Not one step has been taken towards improving the flow of milk from the mammary glands. Only mothers and wet nurses give milk, whereas with time and experimentation every one could give milk and the food problem would be solved

for eternity. We wouldn't even need to sit down to eat:
now and then a step-ladder might be necessary, but nothing more. Why hasn't any one thought of that? Is it so
improbable? Ants have their milk cows—how did that
happen? Anyway, with human milk the universal food,
with manna falling from heaven, and nectar and ambrosia
for dessert, think what a lot of work would be eliminated.
Think too of the gratitude the animals would show, once
they got on to the new scheme of things. All we would
need, men and animals, would be one huge grass plot. No
more dairy companies, no more containers, no more bottles, plates, knives and forks, spoons, pots, pans, stoves.
The solution of the food problem would throw a monkey
wrench into the entire economic and social system; our
mores would change, our religions would disappear, our
money become valueless. One can hardly imagine what
the cause for war would then be, though doubtless a good
excuse will always be found.

Outside of the foreign quarters, then, take it for granted
that there is no good bread to be had. Every foreign group
has introduced into our life some good substantial bread,
even the Scandinavians. (Excepting the English, I should
add, but then we hardly think of them as foreign, though
why we shouldn't I don't know, for when you think of it
the English are even less like us than the Poles or Lat-
vians.) In a Jewish restaurant you usually have a basket
filled with all kinds of bread from which to choose. In a
typical American restaurant, should you ask for rye, whole
wheat or any other kind of bread but the insidious unwholesome, and unpalatable white, you get white bread.
If you insist on rye bread you get whole wheat. If you
insist on whole wheat you get graham bread. Once in a
great while you come upon nut bread; this is always a
sheer accident. Raisin bread is a sort of decoy to lure you
into eating unpalatable, perfidious and debilitating white
bread. When in doubt go to a Jewish restaurant or delicatessen; if necessary, stand up and eat a sandwich made
of sour rye, sweet butter, pastrami and pickle. A Jewish
sandwich contains more food value than an eighty-five
cent meal in the ordinary American restaurant. With a
glass of water to wash it down you can walk away feeling

fit. Don't sit down and eat a Jewish meal, because the Jews are bad cooks despite their great concern about food, which amounts to a neurosis. It is curious, though, how the desire to survive has made the Jews keen about preserving the staff of life. It is even more curious that they are just as much riddled with disease as the other members of the community—more so, in fact, judging purely from personal observation. They not only have all the physical ailments which other white peoples are heir to but they have all the mental and nervous ailments. Often they have everything at once, and then they concentrate upon food with even greater acuity and despair. It is only when they become revolutionary that they begin to lose interest in food. The real American, on the other hand, though totally unrevolutionary at heart, seems born with an indifference to food. One can serve a white American food which would make an Igorote turn up his nose. Americans can eat garbage, provided you sprinkle it liberally with ketchup, mustard, chili sauce, tabasco sauce, cayenne pepper, or any other condiment which destroys the original flavor of the dish. On the other hand, olive oil which the French eschew when preparing salads because it has too strong a flavor, Americans hardly ever use in their salads. Nothing on God's earth is more uninviting, more anaemic, than the American salad. At its best it is like refined puke. The lettuce is a joke: even a canary would refuse to touch it. This concoction, mind you, is usually served before the meal, together with the coffee which is cold by the time you are ready to drink it. The moment you sit down at a table in the ordinary American restaurant, the moment you begin scanning the menu, the waitress asks you what you wish to drink. (If by chance you should say "cocoa" the whole kitchen would be thrown out of gear.) To this question I usually counter with another: "Do you have anything but white bread?" If the answer is not a flat No, it is: "We have whole wheat," or "We have graham bread." Whereupon I usually mumble under my breath: "You can stick that up your ass! When she says: "What did you say?" I reply, "Do you have rye bread by any chance?" Then, before she can say no, I launch into an elaborate explanation of the fact that I don't mean by rye bread the ordinary rye bread, which is no better than white, graham, or whole wheat, but a succulent, tasty, dark, sour rye such as the Russians and the Jews serve. At the mention of these two suspect nationalities a scowl spreads over her face. While she is saying in her most sarcastic voice that she is sorry but they do not have that kind of rye bread or any rye bread, for that matter, I begin asking about the fruit, what kinds of fruit, fresh fruit, they have on hand, knowing damned well that they haven't any. Nine times out of ten her answer will be: "We have apple pie, and peach pie." ("Stick it up your ass!") "I beg your pardon?" she says. "Yes, fruit . . . you know, the kind that grows on trees . . . apples, pears, bananas, plums, oranges . . . something with skin on it that you peel." Whereupon a light dawns and she hastens to interpolate: "Oh, but we have apple sauce!" ("Fuck your apple sauce!") "I beg pardon?" Here I look leisurely round the room, surveying the shelves, the counter, the pie plates. Finally, resting my gaze upon a bowl of artificial fruit, I exclaim with glee: "Like that over there, *only real!*"

Sometimes, upon scanning the menu and knowing that it will only give me a belly-ache, I ask immediately if they can serve me a large bowl of fresh fruit. Here, incidentally, let me call attention to the dishes of mixed fruit prepared early in the morning which stand rotting in disgusting sweet canned juices until lunch or dinner hour. In the Automat type of restaurant one sees the counter piled with these vile stews. These, like the salads mentioned a moment ago, and like the pies fabricated by the wholesale bakers (who are probably responsible for more deaths than all our wars put together), are peculiar to the American temperament. There is not the least food value in any of them. The salad is at its worst when served in one of those delightful little inns run by spinsters in villages of imaginary charm, such as one is supposed to find in Vermont, Maryland, or Connecticut. Here everything looks immaculate and is immaculate, and therefore without value, without flavor, without joy. One suddenly feels like a canary which has been castrated and can no longer warble or differentiate between seed and salad. Beginning with this obscene salad one just knows that the meal is going to end with a charming little dessert such as prune whip or vanilla ice cream. To ask for a grape or a herring in one of these places is like committing sacrilege. There are certain things you must never ask for in an American restaurant. Never. One is good sour rye such as the Russians and the Jews make. Another is a cup of strong coffee. (Exceptions: French and Italian restaurants, and Louisiana. In Louisiana you can get a cup of coffee that is like liquid dynamite. But it tastes good; it has chicory in it. And chicory is excellent, despite all opinion to the contrary.) A third is cheese. A fourth is grapes. A fifth is nuts. Never have I seen a bowl of assorted and uncracked nuts put on the table in an American restaurant. Now and then, rarely, very rarely, one sees nuts in an American home. Usually, however, they are there as decoration. The fruit likewise. Fruit and nuts belong on the sideboard for the children, when there are any, to nibble at. The mixed fruit, or fruit salad, as they have the impudence to call it in America, reaches the height of abomination in the arm-chair Automat type of restaurant. Have you ever noticed the derelicts who frequent these eating places, sitting in the show window munching their lunch or dinner? Is there any more lugubrious sight on earth? (The corollary to it is the cheap traveling salesman type of hotel where all day long the weary commercial traveler sits in an enormous leather armchair staring vacantly out on the street. This is the type who gets orders for useless commodities which the American slave toils his ass off to accumulate, which he sells to his own kind and pretends thereby that he is earning an honest living. This is the type that votes the Democratic or Republican ticket year in and year out, in lean years and fat years, in war and in peace, and is always complaining that business is bad. This is the most traveled man in the world, and yet he knows nothing, absolutely nothing, and brags about it. This is the type who when you mention China says immediately—"coolies." If there is any more ignominious coolie than the traveling salesman I have yet to know him. The fact that he reads the "Digest" or some other compilation of facts gives him the illusion that he is informed and a useful member of society.)

But it's the pie that takes the cake. The pie is at its worst in the Greek restaurant, often called "New York Café," and encountered in every village and hamlet throughout the length and breadth of the land. In fact, everything is at its worst in this type of eating place. But it's here that the pie becomes positively obsessive. Often there is nothing to offer the weary traveler but pie. There they stand, row upon row of pie plates, all filled with gangrene and arsenic. The crust looks like scurf and is scurf, usually of the finest rancid grease made by the Criscomaniacs of America. Here and there one can detect in a whole pie a piece of fruit, such as apple or peach; it is surrounded by a clot of phlegm swimming in a mess of undefinable paste. The piece of apple or peach is sourish, bilious, gaseous, having no more resemblance to the apple or peach in its native state than corn whiskey has to corn on the cob. The Greek proprietor delights in serving white Americans this unholy dish; he despises them for eating it, but, canny business man that he is, he believes in giving them what they ask for. He himself has a totally different cuisine, a damned good one, too, I must say, if you ever make a friend of him and get invited to his home. On his table you will see olives, real olives, okra, olive oil, fruits of all kinds, nuts, rice, vine leaves, the tenderest lamb imaginable, wines of all kind, including retsina, and cognac, Greek cognac, and other delicacies.

Let us digress here a moment. . . . How is it that Americans, composed of nothing but foreign nationalities, living amongst people accustomed to the most varied cuisines, people who have made an art of cooking from time immemorial, continue to be the worst cooks in the world, continue to open one foul restaurant after another? Explain it, if you can. To me it's an enigma. The more mixed becomes the blood in our veins, the more American we become. And by American I mean the more set, crass, conservative, prejudiced, stupid, narrow-minded, unexperimental and unrevolutionary. In every big city we have Chinese, Italian, French, Hungarian, Russian, German, Swedish restaurants. Do we learn anything from these skilled restaurateurs? No, not a thing. We go our way, serving pies, mixed fruit salads, hamburgers, baked beans, steak and onions, vicious veal cutlets, whether breaded or unbreaded, and so on. Has any one ever had a good stew in an American restaurant? The peasants of Europe have thrived on stews for centuries. Here a stew means a couple of spoonfuls of superannuated meat swimming in a tiny pool of grease and bilge with bloated potatoes as a garniture. One hasn't begun to eat when the meal is over. It's an imaginary stew at the best. And the most imaginary part of it is the vegetables without which no stew is complete: leeks, carrots, turnips, onions, celery, parsley, and so on. If you find a tiny piece of any other vegetable than the potato you are indeed a lucky individual.

All right, steak then! Steak is the great American dish. Steak and onions. Fine. Nothing better, I say. Where can you get it? I mean without paying $2.50 per person! The first and only time I got the real flavor of steak was when I passed through Denver. Up till then I never knew what a real steak tasted like. The meat companies are for convincing us that meat from the refrigerator, meat that has been on ice several years, is the best meat of all. The whole world is being shipped and fed this cold storage meat, thanks to Armour & Co. and their subsidiary hog-butchers. In France I used to eat *filet de boeuf* practically every other day. It cost, for one person, a good portion, mind you, from twelve to eighteen cents, at the rate of exchange prevailing in the late thirties. It was delicious meat, and I knew how to prepare it (Americans as a rule know only how to spoil a good piece of meat in cooking it.) When I came to America, in 1940, I went to the butcher one day and asked for my customary *filet de boeuf*. A piece for two people came to $1.10, so help me God. I couldn't believe my ears. And this was in a cheap butcher shop on Third Avenue, New York. Christ only knows what it would have cost in the Park Avenue neighborhood. I took it home and I fried it. I did everything just as I used to at the Villa Seurat. I had wine with it too, the best I could buy for $1.25 the bottle. I also had grapes and nuts, and a salad prepared with the best olive oil. I had several kinds of cheese, including roquefort and camembert. Despite all precautions the meal didn't taste the same. There was something lacking. As a matter of fact, all the essentials were lacking. A piece of lettuce grown in America is like a piece of lettuce grown in

France only in looks and name. American fruit, the most sensational looking fruit in the world (barring the tropics), is practically tasteless compared to the sicklier looking European fruits. American cheeses look delicious, and God knows the Kraft Brothers have tickled them up inordinately, but they do not have the flavor of the cheeses they are made to imitate. A stale piece of Camembert in a dirty French restaurant is worth a whole box of beautiful looking fresh Camembert put out by the crafty cheese-makers of Wisconsin. The flat Dutch cheeses are of course still more flat and tasteless when you eat them in America, being as they are the product of the most pampered cows in all the world. Wines, even when they are good, and in the realm of ordinary table wines America makes some of the best, do not taste as good as in Europe, perhaps because the atmosphere, the violence, the tempo of American life destroys whatever blessing wine confers.

Wine with the meal, in America, produces the wrong result. What is required, when attempting to digest American food, is strong spirits—whiskey, gin, cocktails. The correct procedure is to get soused beforehand; this enables one to eat without noticing how vile the food is. It gets one flushed and excited, and the food is forgotten. It makes one argumentative, which aids in bringing on indigestion, dyspepsia, flatulence, constipation, hemorrhoids, and finally the operating table. Whichever road you take, in America, you always wind up at the surgeon's door. If you buy an automobile it's the surgeon you have to reckon with eventually. If you take a good-paying job, it's the surgeon who will bleed you to death. If you economize and eat in armchair restaurants, or the Greek restaurants (where American food is served—not the real Greek restaurant), you meet the surgeon sooner or later, generally sooner. If you take to the soil and live the outdoor life, you first must have all your teeth pulled out and plates inserted. Farmers have about the worst teeth of all, even worse than factory workers. They have all the physical ailments, too, and are often as not undernourished. Farmers die of inanition in the midst of plenty. There isn't anything you can do, in America, by way of earning a living whereby you can escape dire taxation, disease, accident, misery and humiliation. At the end of every road stands the surgeon, who is for Americans what Nemesis was for the Greeks. The whole culture of America springs from two lunatics: the Marquis de Sade and Sacher Masoch. Justice, always retributive, is apotheosized by the surgeon. His henchmen are the dentists. If you have an ache or pain never mention it to the dentist, or he will immediately extract all your teeth. Nowadays even cowboys are proud of their false teeth. Scarcely any hard-working American, however splendid his physique, is without plates or bridges after forty. Hardly any normal American has a full head of hair after forty. Hardly any American over twenty-one, whether he works hard or takes it easy, is without eye-glasses. Almost every American suffers from hemorrhoids. Practically every American over forty has a bad heart. Cancer, syphilis, arthritis, tuberculosis, schizophrenia are so prevalent that we accept them as part of the bargain—i. e., the American way of life. Nearly every family boasts of one moron among its members, one lunatic, one drunkard, one pervert. All the food advertisements boast of the vitamin contents of their products. All the medicaments advertised boast of their cure for every thing under the sun. It is obvious that our foods lack the proper vitamins, just as it is obvious that in employing these health foods so rich in vitamins we nevertheless are afflicted with all the diseases known to man. We die young, mortgaged to the hilt, insolvent, despite all the insurance policies issued by all the insurance companies whose tentacles reach into every avenue of commercial and industrial life. It is also evident that, despite the fact this is the land of opportunity where freedom reigns, where every one has the right to worship and the right to vote for the wrong candidate, that the zest for life is so low that less than one child per family is now produced, except among certain Indian tribes, certain religious communities, certain strata of poor whites, and among the Negroes as a whole. Even the Jews, known for their big families as well as their good bread, are beginning to have less children—in America. And when the Jew loses his desire to perpetuate his own kind there must indeed be something seriously wrong with the national life. In the poorest countries of Europe the Jews still remained fertile;

here, with everything in his grasp, except recognition by the Gentiles, he withers away. Only among the American Indians, and there only in certain tribes, is the population on the increase. It is said that this is due in part to the practice of polygamy. And here we touch another tender subject, one almost as potent as bread. I mean the fear among native white Americans of indulging in any other form of marriage but that sponsored by the Christian churches. Why not polygamy? Why not polyandry? Why not any kind of marriage, including love marriages? With polygamy the Mormons were fast on the way to building an empire. Nobody can say that the Mormons are, or ever were, an undesirable element in the great American community. They were and still are one of the few communities in this country where poverty is relatively unknown. They produce less criminals than other parts of the country—and less morons, and less idiots, and less trouble of any nature. And God knows they were never, never more immoral than the other members of the community. On the contrary, they were not only more law-abiding, more peaceful, more prosperous, more social-minded and far-visioned than the other communities of America, but they were absolutely more moral in the strictest sense of the word, that is, in the sense that they actually practiced what they preached.

But to get back to bread . . . Today the mailman brought three kinds of bread: Italian bread, a milk loaf, and pumpernickel. (No sour rye, of course, no corn bread.) The bread comes from Monterey, the nearest town, which is fifty miles away. In Monterey there is no Jewish grocer or delicatessen, worse luck. In Monterey there are Mexicans, Portuguese and Filipinos, but who gives a damn what these poor devils eat? The Mexicans have their tortillas, the Portuguese their garlic, and the Filipinos . . . well, among other things they have all our bad habits. Nobody in Monterey has a good slice of bread to eat. Nor in Carmel either, unless it's Robinson Jeffers, and that would be a sacramental bread. Just outside of Carmel lives Edward Weston, the photographer. And that leads me to speak of another kind of bread: photographic bread. Have you ever noticed that even the photographic bread tastes poorly? Have you ever seen a piece of bread photographed by our advertising maniacs which you would like to bite into? I haven't. Edward Weston could undoubtedly make you the most wonderful photographic bread conceivable—*but could you eat it?* The bread you hang on your wall is not the bread you want to eat at table. Even a piece of bread by Man Ray would prove unpalatable, particularly if he just happened to be reading his favorite author, the Marquis de Sade. Sacher Masoch might have made a good bread, if he had lived long enough. It has a Kosher sound, *Sacher Masoch*. But in the long run I have a feeling it would make one morbid and introspective, this Sacher Masoch bread.

I have now found that the only way to cat our most unwholesome, unpalatable and unappetizing American bread, the staff of our unsavory and monotonous life, is to adopt the following procedure. This is a recipe, so please follow instructions to the letter.

To begin with, accept any loaf that is offered you without question, even if it is not wrapped in cellophane, even if it contains no kelp. Throw it in the back of the car with the oil can and the grease rags; if possible, bury it under a sack of coal, *bituminous coal*. As you climb up the road to your home, drop it in the mud a few times and dig your heels into it. If you have a dog with you, let him pee on it now and then. When you get to the house, and after you have prepared the other dishes, take a huge carving knife and rip the loaf from stem to stern. Then take one whole onion, peeled or unpeeled, one carrot, one stalk of celery, one huge piece of garlic, one sliced apple, a herring, a handful of anchovies, a sprig of parsley, and an old toothbrush and shove them into the disemboweled guts of the bread. Over these pour first a thimbleful of kerosene, a dash of Lavoris and just a wee bit of Clorox; then sprinkle guts liberally with the following—molasses, honey, orange marmalade, vanilla, soy bean sauce, tabasco sauce, ketchup and arnica. Over this add a layer of chopped nuts, assorted nuts, of course, a few bay leaves (whole), some marjoram, and a stick of licorice cut into fine pieces. Put the loaf in the oven for ten minutes and serve. If it is still lacking in taste whip up a chili con carne piping hot and mix bread well with it until it becomes a thick gruel. If this fails, piss on it and throw it to the dog. But under no circumstances feed it to the birds. The birds of North America are already on the decline, as I pointed out earlier. Their beaks have become dull, their wingspan shortened; they are pining and drooping, moulting in season and out. Above all, they no longer sing as they used to; they make sour notes, they bleat instead of tweeting, and sometimes, when the fogs set in, they have been heard to cackle and wheeze.

MAX

THERE ARE SOME PEOPLE whom you call immediately by
their first name. Max is one of them. There are people to
whom you feel immediately attracted, not because you like
them, but because you detest them. You detest them so
heartily that your curiosity is aroused; you come back to
them again and again to study them, to arouse in yourself
a feeling of compassion which is really absent. You do
things for them, not because you feel any sympathy for
them, but because their suffering is incomprehensible to
you.

I remember the evening Max stopped me on the boulevard. I remember the feeling of repugnance which his face,
his whole manner inspired. I was hurrying along, on my
way to the cinema, when this sad Jewish face suddenly
blocks my way. He asked me for a light or something—
whatever it was it was only an excuse, I knew. I knew immediately that he was going to pour out a tale of woe, and
I didn't want to hear it. I was curt and brusque, almost
insulting; but that didn't matter, he stuck there, his face
almost glued to mine, and clung like a leech. Without
waiting to hear his story I offered him some change, hoping that he would be disgusted and walk off. But no, he
refused to be offended; he clung to me like a leech.

From that evening on it almost seems as if Max were
dogging my steps. The first few times I ran into him I put
it down to sheer coincidence. Gradually, however, I became suspicious. Stepping out of an evening I would ask

myself instinctively—"where now? are you sure Max won't be there?" If I were going for a stroll I would pick an absolutely strange neighborhood, one that Max would never dream of frequenting. I knew that he had to maintain a more or less fixed itinerary—the grand boulevards, Montparnasse, Montmartre, wherever the tourists were apt to congregate. Towards the end of the evening Max would disappear from my mind completely. Strolling home, along an accustomed route, I would be entirely oblivious of Max. Then, as sure as fate, probably within a stone's throw of my hotel, out he'd pop. It was weird. He'd always bob up head on, as it were, and how he got there suddenly like that I never could figure out. Always I'd see him coming towards me with the same expression, a mask which I felt he had clapped on expressly for me. The mask of sorrow, of woe, of misery, lit up by a little wax taper which he carried inside him, a sort of holy, unctuous light that he had stolen from the synagogue. I knew always what his first words would be and I would laugh as I uttered them, a laugh which he always interpreted as a sign of friendliness.

"How *are* you, Miller!" he would say, just as though we hadn't seen each other for years. And with this *how are you* the smile which he had clapped on would broaden and then, quite suddenly, as though he had put a snuffer over the little wax taper inside him, it would go out. With this would come another familiar phrase—"*Miller,* do you know what has happened to me since I saw you?" I knew very well that *nothing* had happened in the interim. But I knew also, from experience, that soon we would be sitting down somewhere to enjoy the experience of *pretending* that something had happened in the interim. Even though he had done nothing but walks his legs off, in the interim, that would be something new that had happened to him. If the weather had been warm, or if it had been cold, *that* would be something that had happened to him. Or if he had managed to get a day's work that too would be something. Everything that happened to him was of a bad nature. It couldn't be otherwise. He lived in the expectation that things would grow worse, and of course they always did.

I had grown so accustomed to Max, to his state of perpetual misfortune, that I began to accept him as a natural phenomenon: he was a part of the general landscape, like rocks, trees, urinals, brothels, meat markets, flower stalls, and so on. There are thousands of men like Max roaming the streets, but Max was the personification of all. He was Unemployment, he was Hunger, he was Misery, he was Woe, he was Despair, he was Defeat, he was Humiliation. The others I could get rid of by flipping them a coin. Not Max! Max was something so close to me that it was just impossible to get rid of him. He was closer to me than a bed-bug. Something *under* the skin, something in the blood-stream. When he talked I only half-listened. I had only to catch the opening phrase and I could continue by myself, indefinitely, *ad infinitum*. Everything he said was true, horribly true. Sometimes I felt that the only way to make known this truth would be to put Max on his back on the sidewalk and leave him there spouting out his horrible truths. And what would happen, should I do that? Nothing. *Nothing.* People have a way of making cute little detours, of stuffing their ears. People don't want to hear these truths. They *can't* hear them, for the reason that they're all talking to themselves in the same way. The only difference is that Max said them aloud, and saying them aloud he made them seem objective, as though he, Max, were only the instrument to reveal the naked truth. He had gotten so far beyond suffering that he had become suffering itself. It was terrifying to listen to him because he, Max, had disappeared, had been swallowed up by his suffering.

It's easier to take man as a symbol than as a fact. Max to me was a symbol of the world, of a condition of the world which is unalterable. Nothing will change it. Nothing! Silly to think of laying Max out on the sidewalk. It would be like saying to people—"Don't you *see?*" See what? The *world?* Sure they see. *The world!* That's what they're trying to escape, trying *not* to see. Every time Max approached me I had this feeling of having the whole world on my hands, of having it right under my nose. The best thing for you, Max, I often thought to myself as I sat listening to him, is to blow your brains out. Destroy yourself! That's the only solution. But you can't get rid of the world so easily. Max is infinite. You would have to kill off every man, woman and child, every tree, rock, house, plant, beast, star. Max is in the blood. He's a disease.

I'm talking all the time about Max as about something in the past. I'm talking about the man I knew a year or so ago, before he went to Vienna—the Max I ran out on, the Max I left flat. The last note I had from him was a desperate plea to bring *"medicaments."* He wrote that he was ill and that they were going to throw him out of the hotel. I remember reading his note and laughing over the broken English. I didn't doubt for a minute that everything he said was true. But I had made up my mind not to lift a finger. I was hoping to Christ he *would* croak and not bother me any more. When a week had passed, and no further word from him, I felt relieved. I hoped he had realized that it was useless to expect anything more of me. And supposing he had died? It made no difference to me either way—I wanted to be left alone.

When it seemed as if I had really shaken him off for good and all I began to think of writing about him. There were moments when I was almost tempted to look him up, in order to corroborate certain impressions which I intended to exploit. I felt so strongly about it that I was on the point several times of paying him to come to see me. That last note of his, about the *"medicaments,"* how I regretted having given it away! With that note in my hands I felt I could bring Max to life again. It's strange now, when I think about it, because everything Max had ever said was deeply engraved in my memory . . . I suppose I wasn't ready to write the story then.

Not long after this I was obliged to leave Paris for a few months. I thought of Max only rarely, and then as though it were a humorous and pathetic incident in the past. I never asked myself—"is he alive? what can he be doing now?" No, I thought of him as a symbol, as something imperishable—not flesh and blood, not a man suffering. Then one night, shortly after my return to Paris, just when I am searching frantically for another man, whom do I run smack into but Max. And what a Max!

"Miller, how *are* you? Where have you *been?"*

It's the same Max only he's unshaved. A Max resurrected from the grave in a beautiful suit of English cut and a heavy velour hat with a brim so stiffly curved that he looks like a mannikin. He gives me the same smile, only it's much fainter now and it takes longer to go out. It's like the light of a very distant star, a star which is giving its last twinkle before fading out forever. And the sprouting beard! It's that no doubt which makes the look of suffering stand out even more forcibly than before. The beard seems to have softened the look of absolute disgust which hung about his mouth like a rotten halo. The disgust has melted away into weariness, and the weariness into pure suffering. The strange thing is that he inspires even less pity in me now than before. He is simply grotesque—a sufferer and a caricature of suffering at the same time. He seems to be aware of this himself. He doesn't talk any more with the same verve; he seems to doubt his own words. He goes through with it only because it's become a routine. He seems to be waiting for me to laugh, as I used to. In fact, he laughs himself now, as though the Max he was talking about were another Max.

The suit, the beautiful English suit which was given him by an Englishman in Vienna and which is a mile too big for him! He feels ridiculous in it and humiliated. Nobody believes him any more—*not in the beautiful English suit!* He looks down at his feet which are shod in a pair of low canvas shoes; they look dirty and worn, the canvas shoes. They don't go with the suit and the hat. He's on the point of telling me that they're comfortable nevertheless, but force of habit quickly prompts him to add that his other shoes are at the cobbler's and that he hasn't the money to get them out. It's the English suit, however, that's preying on his mind. It's become for him the visible symbol of his new misfortune. While holding his arm out so that I may examine the cloth he's already telling me what happened to him in the interim, how he managed to get to Vienna where he was going to start a new life and how he found it even worse there than in Paris. The soup kitchens were cleaner, that he had to admit. But grudgingly. What good is it if the soup kitchens are clean and you haven't even a sou in your pocket? But it was beautiful, Vienna, and clean—so *clean!* He can't get over it. But tough! Everybody is on the bum there. But it's so clean and beautiful, it would make you cry, he adds.

Is this going to be a long story, I'm wondering. My friends are waiting for me across the street, and besides, there's a man I must find . . .

"Yes, Vienna," I say absent-mindedly, trying to scan the terrasse out of the corner of my eye.

"No, not Vienna. Basle!" he shouts. *"Basle!"*

"I left Vienna over a month ago," I hear him saying.

"Yes, yes, and what happened then?"

"What happened? I told you, Miller, they took my papers away from me. I *told* you, they made a tourist out of me!"

When I hear this I burst out laughing. Max laughs too in his sad way. "Can you imagine such a thing," he says. "I should be a *tourist!"* He gives another dingy chortle.

Of course that wasn't all. At Basle, it seems, they pulled him off the train. Wouldn't let him cross the frontier.

"I says to them—what's the matter, please? Am I not *en règle?"*

All his life, I forgot to mention, Max has been fighting to be *en règle.* Anyway, they yank him off the train and they leave him there, in Basle, stranded. What to do? He walks down the main drive looking for a friendly face—an American, or an Englishman at least. Suddenly he sees a sign: *Jewish Boarding House.* He walks in with his little valise, orders a cup of coffee and pours out his tale of woe. They tell him not to worry—it's nothing.

"Well, anyway, you're back again," I say, trying to break away.

"And what good does it do me?" says Max. "They made me a tourist now, so what should I do for work? *Tell me,* Miller! And with such a suit like this can I bum a nickel any more? I'm finished. If only I shouldn't look so well!"

I look him over from head to toe. It's true, he does look incongruously well off. Like a man just out of a sick bed—glad to be up again, but not strong enough to shave. And then the hat! A ridiculously expensive hat that weighs a ton—and silk-lined! It makes him look like a man from the old country. And the stub of a beard! If it were just a little longer he'd look like one of those sad, virtuous, abstract-looking wraiths who flit through the ghettoes of Prague and Budapest. Like a holy man. The brim of the hat curls up so stiffly, so *ethically*. Purim and the holy men a little tipsy from the good wine. Sad Jewish faces trimmed with soft beards. And a Joe Welch hat to top it off! The tapers burning, the rabbi chanting, the holy wail from the standees, and everywhere hats, hats, all turned up at the brim and making a jest of the sadness and woe.

"Well, anyway, you're back again," I repeat. I'm shaking hands with him but he doesn't drop my hand. He's in Basle again, at the Jewish Boarding House, and they're telling him how to slip across the border. There were guards everywhere and he doesn't know how it happened but as they passed a certain tree and since no one came out it was safe and he went ahead. "And like that," he says, "I'm in Paris again. Such a lousy place as it is! In Vienna they were clean at least. There were professors and students on the bread line, but here they are nothing but bums, and such lousy bums, they give you bugs right away."

"Yes, yes, that's how it is, Max," and I'm shaking his hand again.

"You know, Miller, sometimes I think I am going mad. I don't sleep any more. At six o'clock I am wide awake already and thinking on what to do. I can't stay in the room when it comes light. I must go down in the street. Even if I am hungry I must walk, I must see people. I can't stay alone any more. Miller, for God's sake, can you see what is happening to me? I wanted to send you a card from Vienna, just to show you that Max remembered you, but I couldn't think on your address. *And how was it,* Miller, in New York? Better than here, I suppose? No? The *crise,* too? Everywhere it's the *crise.* You can't escape. They won't give you to work and they won't give you to eat. What can you do with such bastards? Sometimes, Miller, I get so frightened . . ."

"Listen, Max, I've got to go now. Don't worry, you won't kill yourself . . . *not yet.*"

He smiles. "Miller," he says, "you have such a good nature. You are so happy all the time. Miller, I wish I could be with you always. I would go anywhere in the world with you . . . *anywhere*."

This conversation took place about three nights ago. Yesterday at noon I was sitting on the terrasse of a little café in an out of the way spot. I chose the spot deliberately so as not to be disturbed during the reading of a manuscript. An *aperitif* was before me—I had taken but a sip or two. Just as I am about half-way through the manuscript I hear a familiar voice. "Why *Miller*, how *are* you?" And there, as usual, bending over me is Max. The same peculiar smile, the same hat, the same beautiful suit and canvas shoes. Only now he's shaved.

I invite him to sit down. I order a sandwich and a glass of beer for him. As he sits down he shows me the pants to his beautiful suit—he has a rope around his waist to hold them up. He looks at them disgustedly, then at the dirty canvas shoes. Meanwhile he's telling me what happened to him in the interim. All day yesterday, so he says, nothing to eat. Not a crumb. And then, as luck would have it, he bumped into some tourists and they asked him to have a drink. "I had to be polite," he says. "I couldn't tell them right away I was hungry. I kept waiting and waiting for them to eat, but they had already eaten, the bastards. The whole night long I am drinking with them and nothing in my belly. Can you imagine such a thing, that they shouldn't eat once the whole night long?"

To-day I'm in the mood to humor Max. It's the manuscript I've been reading over. Everything was so well put . . . I can hardly believe I wrote the damned thing.

"Listen, Max, I've got an old suit for you, if you want to trot home with me!"

Max's face lights up. He says immediately that he'll keep the beautiful English suit for Sundays. Have I an iron at home, he would like to know. Because he's going to press my suit for me . . . *all my suits*. I explain to him that I haven't any iron, *but* I may have still another suit. (It just occurred to me that somebody promised me a suit the other day.) Max is in ecstasy. That makes *three* suits he'll have. He's pressing them up, in his mind. They must have a good crease in them, his suits. You can tell an American right away, he tells me, by the crease in his trousers. Or if not by the crease, by the walk. That's how he spotted me the first day, he adds. And the hands in the pockets! A Frenchman never keeps his hands in his pockets.

"So you're sure you'll have the other suit too?" he adds quickly.

"I'm fairly sure, Max . . . Have another sandwich— and another demi!"

"Miller," he says, "you always think of the right things. It isn't so much what you give me—it's the way you think it out. You give me *courage*."

Courage. He pronounces it the French way. Every now and then a French word drops into his phrases. The French words are like the velour hat; they are incongruous. Especially the word *misère*. No Frenchman ever put such *misère* into *misère*. Well, anyway, *courage!* Again he's telling me that he'd go anywhere in the world with me. We'd come out all right, the two of us. (And me wondering all the time how to get rid of him!) But to-day it's O. K. To-day I'm going to do things for you, Max! He doesn't know, the poor devil, that the suit I'm offering him is too big for me. He thinks I'm a generous guy and I'm going to let him think so. To-day I want him to worship me. It's the manuscript I was reading a few moments ago. It was so good, what I wrote, that I'm in love with myself.

"*Garçon!* A package of cigarettes—*pour le monsieur!*"

That's for Max. Max is a *monsieur* for the moment. He's looking at me with that wan smile again. Well, *courage,* Max! To-day I'm going to lift you to heaven—and then drop you like a sinker! Jesus, just one more day I'll waste on this bastard and then bango! I'll put the skids under him. To-day I'm going to listen to you, you bugger . . . listen to every nuance. I'll extract the last drop of juice— and then, *overboard you go!*

"Another *demi,* Max? Go on, have another . . . just one more! And have another sandwich!"

"But *Miller,* can you *afford* all that?"

He knows damned well I can afford it, else I wouldn't urge him. But that's his line with me. He forgets I'm not one of the guys on the boulevards, one of his regular cli-

Ronald Dunkin

1. Tony and Valentine Miller. Big Sur, 1958.

Nick Cominos

2. Valentine, Henry and Tony Miller. Big Sur, 1957.

Arthur Knight

3. Henry Miller.

4. Eve Miller on patio outside house. Big Sur, 1957.

Larry Colwell

Wynn Bullock

5. Henry Miller and Alfred Perlès. Big Sur, 1954.

entèle. Or maybe he puts me in the same category—how should *I* know?

The tears are coming to his eyes. Whenever I see that I grow suspicious. Tears! Genuine little tears from the tear-jerker. Pearls, every one of them. Jesus, if only I could get inside that mechanism for once and see how he does it!

It's a beautiful day. Marvellous wenches passing by. Does Max ever notice them, I wonder.

"I say, Max, what do you do for a lay now and then?"

"For a *what?*" he says.

"You heard me. For a *lay!* Don't you know what a lay is?"

He smiles—that wan, wistful smile—again. He looks at me sidewise, as though a little surprised that I should put such a question to him. With *his* misery, *his* suffering, should he, Max, be guilty of such thoughts? Well, yes, to tell the truth, he does have such thoughts now and then. It's human, he says. But then, for ten francs, what can you expect? It makes him disgusted with himself. He would rather . . .

"Yes, I know, Max. I know exactly what you mean . . ."

I take Max along with me to the publisher's. I let him wait in the courtyard while I go inside. When I come out I have a load of books under my arm. Max makes a dive for the package—it makes him feel good to carry the books, to do some real work.

"Miller, I think you will be a great success some day," he says. "You don't have to write such a wonderful book—sometimes it's just luck."

"That's it, Max, it's sheer luck. Just luck, that's all!"

We're walking along the Rue de Rivoli under the arcade. There's a book shop somewhere along here where my book is on display. It's a little cubby-hole and the window is full of books wrapped in bright cellophane. I want Max to have a look at my book in the window. I want to see the effect it will produce.

Ah, here's the place! We bend down to scan the titles. There's the *Kama Sutra* and *Under the Skirt, My Life and Loves,* and *Down There* . . . But where's *my* book? It used to be on the top shelf, next to a queer book on flagellation.

Max is studying the jacket illustrations. He doesn't seem to care whether my book is there or not.

"Wait a minute, Max, I'm going inside."

I open the door impetuously. An attractive young Frenchwoman greets me. I give a quick, desperate glance at the shelves. "Have you got the *Tropic of Cancer?*" I ask. She nods her head immediately and points it out to me. I feel somewhat relieved. I inquire if it's selling well. And did she ever read it herself? Unfortunately she doesn't read English. I fiddle around hoping to hear a little more about my book. I ask her why it's wrapped in cellophane. She explains why. Still I haven't had enough. I tell her that the book doesn't belong in a shop like this—it's not that kind of book, you know.

She looks at me rather queerly now. I think she's beginning to doubt if I really am the author of the book, as I said I was. It's difficult to make a point of contact with her. She doesn't seem to give a damn about my book or any other book in the shop. It's the French in her, I suppose . . . I ought to be getting along. I just realize that I haven't shaved, that my pants are not pressed and that they don't match my coat. Just then the door opens and a pale, aesthetic-looking young Englishman enters. He seems completely bewildered. I sneak out while he's closing the door.

"Listen, Max, they're inside—a whole row of them! They're selling like hot-cakes. Yes, everybody's asking for the book. That's what she says."

"I told you, Miller, that you would be a success."

He seems absolutely convinced, Max. Too easily convinced to suit me. I feel that I must talk about the book, even to Max. I suggest we have a coffee at the bar. Max is thinking about something. It disturbs me because I don't want him to be thinking about anything but the book for the moment. "I was thinking, Miller," he says abruptly, "that you should write a book about my experiences." He's off again, about his troubles. I shunt it off quickly.

"Look here, Max, I *could* write a book about you, but I don't want to. I want to write about myself. Do you understand?"

Max understands. He knows I have a lot to write about. He says I am a *student*. By that he means, no doubt, a *student of life*. Yes, that's it—a student of life. I must walk around a great deal, go here and there, waste my time, appear to be enjoying myself, while all the time, of course, I am studying life, studying people. Max is beginning to get the idea. It's no cinch being a writer. A twenty-four hour job.

Max is reflecting on it. Making comparisons with his own life—the difference between one kind of misery and another. Thinking of his troubles again, of how he can't sleep, thinking of the machinery inside his bean that never stops.

Suddenly he says: "And the writer, I suppose he has his own nightmares!"

His nightmares! I write that down on an envelope immediately.

"You're writing that down?" says Max. "Why? Was it so good what I said?"

"It was *marvellous,* Max. It's worth money to me, a thought like that."

Max looks at me with a sheepish smile. He isn't sure whether I'm spoofing him or not.

"Yes, Max," I repeat, "it's worth a fortune, a remark like that."

His brain is beginning to labor. He always thought, he starts to explain, that a writer had first to accumulate a lot of facts.

"Not at all, Max! Not at all! The less facts you have the better. Best of all is not to have *any* facts, do you get me?"

Max doesn't get it entirely, but he's willing to be convinced. A sort of magic's buzzing in his brain. "That's what I was always thinking," he says slowly, as if to himself. "A book must come from the *heart*. It must *touch* you . . ."

It's remarkable, I'm thinking, how quickly the mind leaps. Here, in less than a minute, Max has made an important distinction. Why, only the other day Boris and I we spent the whole day talking about this, talking about "the living word." It comes forth with the breath, just the simple act of opening the mouth, *and being with God,* to be sure. Max understands it too, in his way. That the facts

are nothing. Behind the facts there must be the man, *and
the man must be with God,* must talk like God Almighty.

I'm wondering if it might not be a good idea to show
Max my book, have him read a little of it in my presence,
I'd like to see if he gets it. And *Boris!* Maybe it would be
a good idea to present Max to Boris. I'd like to see what
impression Max would make on him. There'd be a little
change in it, too, no doubt. Maybe enough for the both
of us—for dinner . . . I'm explaining to Max, as we
draw near the house, that Boris is a good friend of mine,
another writer like myself. "I don't say that he'll do anything for you, but I want you to meet him." Max is perfectly
willing . . . why not? And then Boris is a Jew, that ought
to make it easier. I want to hear them talking Yiddish. I
want to see Max weep in front of Boris. I want to see Boris
weep too. Maybe Boris will put him up for a while, in the
little alcove upstairs. It would be funny to see the two of
them living together. Max could press his clothes and run
errands for him—and cook perhaps. There's lots of things
he could do—to earn his grub. I try hard not to look too
enthusiastic. "A queer fellow, Boris," I explain to Max.
Max doesn't seem to be at all worried about that. Anyway,
there's no use going into deep explanations. Let them get
together as best they can . . .

Boris comes to the door in a beautiful smoking jacket. He
looks very pale and frail and withdrawn, as though he had
been in a deep reverie. As soon as I mention "Max" his
face lights up. He's heard about Max.

I have a feeling that he's grateful to me for having
brought Max home. Certainly his whole manner is one of
warmth, of sympathy. We go into the studio where Boris
flops on the couch; he throws a steamer blanket over his
frail body. There are two Jews now in a room, face to face,
and both know what suffering is. No need to beat around
the bush. Begin with the suffering . . . plunge right in!
Two kinds of suffering—it's marvellous to me what a contrast they present. Boris lying back on the couch, the most
elegant apostle of suffering that ever I've met. He lies there
like a human Bible on every page of which is stamped the
suffering, the misery, the woe, the torture, the anguish, the

despair, the defeat of the human race. Max is sitting on the edge of his chair, his bald head dented just below the crown, as if suffering itself had come down on him like a sledge-hammer. He's strong as a bull, Max. But he hasn't Boris' strength. He knows only *physical* suffering—hunger, bedbugs, hard benches, unemployment, humiliations. Right now he's geared up to extract a few francs from Boris. He's sitting on the edge of his chair, a bit nervous because we haven't given him a chance yet to explain his case. He wants to tell the story from beginning to end. He's fishing around for an opening. Boris meanwhile is reclining comfortably on his bed of sorrow. He wants Max to take his time. He knows that Max has come to suffer for him.

While Max talks I snoop about looking for a drink. I'm determined to enjoy this seance. Usually Boris says immediately—"what'll you have to drink?" But with Max on hand it doesn't occur to him to offer drinks.

Stone sober and hearing it for the hundredth time Max's story doesn't sound so hot to me. I'm afraid he's going to bore the pants off Boris—with his "facts." Besides, Boris isn't keen on listening to long stories. All he asks for is a little phrase, sometimes just a word. I'm afraid Max is making it all too prosaic. He's in Vienna again, talking about the clean soup kitchens. I know it's going to take a little while before we get to Basle, then Basle to Paris, then Paris, then hunger, want, misery, then full dress rehearsal. I want him to plunge right into the whirlpool, into the stagnant flux, the hungry monotony, the bare, bedbuggy doldrums with all the hatches closed and no fire escapes, no friends, no *sortie,* no-tickee-no-shirtee business. No, Boris doesn't give a damn about continuity; he wants something dramatic, something vitally grotesque and horribly beautiful and true. Max will bore the pants off him, I can see that. . . .

It happens I'm wrong. Boris wants to hear the whole story, from beginning to end. I suppose it's his mood— sometimes he shows an inexhaustible patience. What he's doing, no doubt, is to carry on his own interior monologue. Perhaps he's thinking out a problem while Max talks. It's a rest for him. I look at him closely. Is he listening? Seems to me he's listening all right. He smiles now and then.

Max is sweating like a bull. He's not sure whether he's making an impression or not.

Boris has a way of listening to Max as if he were at the opera. It's better than the opera, what with the couch and the steamer blanket. Max is taking off his coat; the perspiration is rolling down his face. I can see that he's putting his heart and soul into it. I sit at the side of the couch glancing from one to the other. The garden door is open and the sun seems to throw an aureole around Boris' head. To talk to Boris Max has to face the garden. The heat of the afternoon drifts in through the cool studio; it puts a warm, fuzzy aura about Max's words. Boris looks so comfortable that I can't resist the temptation to lie down beside him. I'm lying down now and enjoying the luxury of listening to a familiar tale of woe. Beside me is a shelf of books; I run my eye over them as Max spins it out. Lying down this way, hearing it at full length, I can judge the effect of it better. I catch nuances now that I never caught before. His words, the titles of the books, the warm air drifting in from the garden, the way he sits on the edge of his chair—the whole thing combines to produce the most savory effect.

The room is in a state of complete disorder, as usual. The enormous table is piled with books and manuscripts, with pencilled notes, with letters that should have been answered a month ago. The room gives the impression somehow of a sudden state of arrest, as though the author who inhabited it had died suddenly and by special request nothing had been touched. If I were to tell Max that this man Boris lying on the couch had really died I wonder what he would say. That's exactly what Boris means too—*that he died*. And that's why he's able to listen the way he does, as though he were at the opera. Max will have to die too, in every limb and branch of his body, if he's to survive at all . . . The three books, one next to the other, on the top shelf— almost as if they had been deliberately arranged that way: The Holy Bible, Boris' own book, the Correspondence between Nietzsche and Brandes. Only the other night he was reading to me from the Gospel according to Luke. He says we don't read the Gospels often enough. And then Nietzsche's last letter—*"the crucified one."* Buried in the tomb of the flesh for ten solid years and the whole world singing his praise . . .

Max is talking away. Max the presser. From somewhere near Lemberg he came—near the big fortress. And thousands of them just like him, men with broad triangular faces and puffy underlip, with eyes like two burnt holes in a blanket, the nose too long, the nostrils broad, sensitive, melancholy. Thousands of sad Jewish faces from around Lemberg way, the head thrust deep into the socket of the shoulders, sorrow wedged deep between the strong shoulder blades. Boris is almost of another race, so frail, so light, so delicately attuned. He's showing Max how to write in the Hebrew character; his pen races over the paper. With Max the pen is like a broomstick; he seems to draw the characters instead of inscribing them. The way Boris writes is the way Boris does everything—lightly, elegantly, correctly, definitively. He needs intricacies in order to move swiftly and subtly. Hunger, for instance, would be too coarse, too crude. Only stupid people worry about hunger. The garden, I must say, is also remote to Boris. A Chinese screen would have served just as well—better perhaps. Max, however, is keenly aware of the garden. If you gave Max a chair and told him to sit in the garden he would sit and wait for a week if necessary. Max would ask nothing better than food and a garden . . .

"I don't see what can be done for a man like this," Boris is saying, almost to himself. "It's a hopeless case." And Max is shaking his head in agreement. Max is a case, and he realizes it. But *hopeless*—that I can't swallow. No, nobody is hopeless—not so long as there is a little sympathy and friendship left in the world. The *case* is hopeless, yes. But Max the man . . . no, I can't see it! For Max the man there is still something to be done. There's the next meal, for example, a clean shirt . . . a suit of clothes . . . a bath . . . a shave. Let's not try to solve the *case:* let's do only what's necessary to do immediately. Boris is thinking along the same lines. Only differently. He's saying aloud, just as though Max were not there—"of course, you could give him money . . . but that won't help . . ." *And why not?* I ask myself. Why not money? Why not food, clothing, shelter? *Why not?* Let's start at the bottom, from the ground up.

"Of course," Boris is saying, "if I had met him in Manila I could have done something for him. I could have given him work then . . ."

Manila! Jesus, that sounds grotesque to me! What the hell has Manila got to do with it? It's like saying to a drowning man: "What a pity, what a pity! If you had only let me teach you how to swim!"

Everybody wants to right the world; nobody wants to help his neighbor. They want to make a man of you without taking your body into consideration. It's all cockeyed. And Boris is cockeyed too, asking him *have you any relatives in America?* I know that tack. That's the social worker's first question. Your age, your name and address, your occupation, your religion, and then, very innocent like—*the nearest living relative, please!* As though you hadn't been all over that ground yourself. As though you hadn't said to yourself a thousand times—"I'll die first! I'll die rather than . . ." And they sit there blandly and ask for the secret name, the secret place of shame, and they will go there immediately and ring the door-bell and they will blurt out everything—while you sit at home trembling and sweating with humiliation.

Max is answering the question. Yes, he had a sister in New York. He doesn't know any more where she is. She moved to Coney Island, that's all he knows. Sure, he had no business to leave America. He was earning good money there. He was a presser and he belonged to the union. But when the slack season came and he sat in the park at Union Square he saw that he was nothing. They ride up on their proud horses and they shove you off the sidewalk. For what? For being out of work? Was it *his* fault . . . did he, Max, do anything against the government? It made him furious and bitter; it made him disgusted with himself. What right had they to lay their hands on him? What right had they to make him feel like a worm?

"I wanted to make something of myself," he continues. "I wanted to do something else for a living—not work with my hands all the time. I thought may be I could learn the French and become an *interprète* perhaps."

Boris flashes me a look. I see that that struck home. The dream of the Jew—*not to work with the hands!* The move to Coney Island—another Jewish dream. From the Bronx to Coney Island! From one nightmare to another! Boris himself three times around the globe—but it's always *from the Bronx to Coney Island*. Von Lemberg nach Amerika gehen! Yea, go! On, weary feet! On! On! No rest for you anywhere. No comfort. No end to toil and misery. Cursed you are and cursed you will remain. *There is no hope!* Why don't you fling yourself into his arms? Why don't you? Do you think I will mind? Are you ashamed? Ashamed of what? We know that you are cursed and we can do nothing for you. We pity you, one and all. The wandering Jew! You are face to face with your brother and you withhold the embrace. That is what I can't forgive you for. Look at Max! He is almost your double! Three times around the globe and now you have met yourself face to face. How can you run away from him? Yesterday you were standing there like him, trembling, humiliated, a beaten dog. And now you stand there in a smoking jacket and your pockets are full to bursting. *But you are the same man!* You haven't altered an iota, except to fill your pockets. *Has he a relative in America?* Have *you* a relative in America? Your mother, where is she now? Is she down there in the ghetto still? Is she still in that stinking little room you walked out of when you decided to make a man of yourself? At least you had the satisfaction of succeeding. You killed yourself in order to solve the problem. But if you hadn't succeeded? What then? What if you were standing there now in Max's shoes? Could we send you back to your mother? And what is Max saying? That if only he could find his sister he would throw his arms around her neck, he would work for her until his dying day, he would be her slave, her dog . . . He would work for you too, if you would only give him bread and a place to rest. You have nothing for him to do—I understand that. But can't you *create* something for him to do? Go to Manila, if needs be. Start the racket all over again. But don't ask Max to look for you in Manila three years ago. Max is here now, standing before you. *Don't you see him?*

I turn to Max. "Supposing, Max, you had your choice

. . . I mean suppose you could go wherever you like and start a new life . . . where would you go?"

It's cruel to ask Max a question like that, but I can't stand this hopelessness. Look here, Max, I'm running on, I want you to look at the world as if it belonged to you. Take a look at the map and put your finger on the spot you'd like to be in. What's the use? *What's the use?* you say. Why just this, that if you want to badly enough you can go anywhere in the world. Just by wanting it. Out of desperation you can accomplish what the millionaire is powerless to accomplish. The boat is waiting for you; the country is waiting for you; the job is waiting for you. All things await you if you can but believe it. I haven't a cent, but I can help you to go anywhere you wish. I can go around with the hat and beg for you. Why not? It's easier than if I were asking for myself. Where would you like to go—*Jerusalem? Brazil?* Just say the word, Max, and I'll be off!

Max is electrified. He knows immediately where he'd like to go. And what's more, he almost sees himself going. There's just a little hitch—*the money.* Even that isn't altogether impossible. How much does it take to get to the Argentine? A thousand francs? That's not impossible . . . Max hesitates a moment. It's his age now that worries him. Has he the strength for it? The *moral* strength to begin afresh? He's forty-three now. He says it as if it were old age. (And Titian at 97 just beginning to get a grip on himself, on his art!) Sound and solid he is in the flesh, despite the dent in the back of his skull where the sledge-hammer came down on him. Bald yes, but muscles everywhere, the eyes still clear, the teeth . . . Ah, the teeth! He opens his mouth to show me the rotting stumps. Only the other day he had to go to the dentist—his *gencives* were terribly swollen. And do you know what the dentist said to him? Nervousness! Nothing but nervousness. That scared the life out of him. How should the dentist know that he, Max, was nervous?

Max is electrified. A little lump of courage is forming inside him. Teeth or no teeth, bald, nervous, cockeyed, rheumatic, spavined, what not—what matter? A place to go to, that's the point. *Not Jerusalem!* The English won't let any more Jews in—too many of them already. *Jerusalem for the Jews!* That was when they needed the Jews. Now you must have a good reason for going to Jerusalem—a better reason than just being a Jew. Christ Almighty, what a mockery! If I were a Jew I would tie a rope around my neck and throw myself overboard. Max is standing before me in the flesh. Max the Jew. Can't get rid of him by tying a sinker around his neck and saying: "Jew, go drown yourself!"

I'm thinking desperately. Yes, if I were Max, if I were the beaten dog of a Jew that Max is . . . What then? Yeah, *what?* I can't get anywhere imagining that I'm a Jew. I must imagine simply that I am a man, that I'm hungry, desperate, at the end of my tether.

"Listen, Boris, we've got to do something! *Do* something, do you understand?"

Boris is shrugging his shoulders. Where's all that money going to come from? He's asking *me!* Asking *me* where it's going to come from. All that money. *What* money? A thousand francs . . . two thousand francs . . . *is that money?* And what about that dizzy American Jane who was here a few weeks ago? Not a drop of love she gave you, not the least sign of encouragement. Insulted you right and left—every day. And you handed it out to her. Handed it out like a Croesus. To that little gold-digging bitch of an American. Things like that make me wild, furiously wild. Wouldn't have been so bad if she had been a plain whore. But she was worse than a whore. She bled you and insulted you. Called you a dirty Jew. And you went right on handing it out. It could happen again to-morrow, the same damned thing. Anybody can get it out of you if only they tickle your vanity, if only they flatter the pants off you. You died, you say, and you've been holding one long funeral ever since. But you're not dead, and you know you're not. What the hell does spiritual death matter when Max is standing before you? Die, die, die a thousand deaths—but don't refuse to recognize the living man. Don't make a problem of him. It's flesh and blood, Boris. *Flesh and blood*. He's screaming and you pretend not to hear. You are deliberately making yourself deaf, dumb and blind. You are dead before the living flesh. Dead before your own flesh and blood. You will gain nothing, neither in the spirit, nor in the flesh, if you do not recognize Max your true brother. Your books on the shelf there . . . they stink, your books! What do I care for your sick Nietzsche, for your pale, loving Christ, for your bleeding Dostoievski! Books, books, books. Burn them! They are of no use to you. Better never to have read a line than to stand now in your two shoes and helplessly shrug your shoulders. Everything Christ said is a lie, everything Nietzsche said is a lie, if you don't recognize the word *in the flesh*. They were foul and lying and diseased if you can derive a sweet comfort from them and not see this man rotting away before your very eyes. Go, go to your books and bury yourself! Go back to your Middle Ages, to your Kabbala, to your hair-splitting, angel-twisting geometry. We need nothing of you. We need a breath of life. We need hope, courage, illusion. We need a penny's worth of human sympathy.

We're upstairs now in my place and the bath water is running. Max has stripped down to his dirty underwear; his shirt with the false front is lying over the arm-chair. Undressed he looks like a gnarled tree, a tree that has painfully learned to walk. The man of the sweat shop with his dickey slung over the arm-chair. The powerful body twisted by toil. From Lemberg to America, from the Bronx to Coney Island—hordes and hordes of them, broken, twisted, spavined, as though they had been stuck on a spit and the struggle useless because struggle or no struggle they will sooner or later be eaten alive. I see all these Maxes at Coney Island on a Sunday afternoon: miles and miles of clear beach polluted with their broken bodies. They make a sewer of their own sweat and they bathe in it. They lie on the beach, one on top of the other, entangled like crabs and seaweed. Behind the beach they throw up their ready-made shacks, the combination bath, toilet and kitchen which serves as a home. At six o'clock the alarm goes off; at seven they're in the subway elbow to elbow, and the stench is powerful enough to knock a horse down.

While Max is taking his bath I lay out some clean things for him. I lay out the suit that was given to me, the suit which is too big for me and which he will thank me for profusely. I lie down to think things over calmly. The next

move? We were all going to have dinner together over in
the Jewish quarter, near St. Paul. Then suddenly Boris
changed his mind. He remembered an engagement he had
made for dinner. I wangled a little change out of him for
dinner. Then, as we were parting, he handed Max a little
dough. "Here, Max, I want you to take this," he said,
fishing it out of his jeans. It made me wince to hear him
say that—and to hear Max thanking him profusely. I *know*
Boris. I know this is his worst side. And I forgive him for
it. I forgive him easier than I can forgive myself. I don't
want it to be thought that Boris is mean and hard-hearted.
He looks after his relatives, he pays his debts, he cheats
nobody. If he happens to bankrupt a man he does it according to the rules; he's no worse here than a Morgan or a
Rockefeller. He plays the game, as they say. But *life,* life
he doesn't see as a game. He wins out in every sphere only
to discover in the end that he's cheated himself. With Max
just now he won out handsomely. He got off by squeezing
out a few francs for which he was handsomely thanked.
Now that he's alone with himself he's probably cursing
himself. To-night he'll spend twenty times what he gave
Max, in order to wipe out his guilt.

Max has called me to the bathroom to ask if he can use
my hairbrush. Sure, use it! (To-morrow I'll get a new one!)
And then I look at the bath tub, the last bit of water gurgling through the drain. The sight of those filthy cruds
floating at the bottom of the tub almost makes me puke.
Max is bending over the tub to clean the mess. He's got
the dirt off his hide at last; he feels good, even if he must
mop up his own dirt. I know the feeling. I remember the
public baths in Vienna, the stench that knocks you
down . . .

Max is stepping into his clean linen. He's smiling now—
a different sort of smile than I ever saw him give. He's
standing in his clean underwear and browsing through my
book. He's reading that passage about Boris, about Boris
being lousy and me shaving his arm-pits, about the flag
being at half-mast and everybody dead, including myself.
That was something to go through—and come out *singing.*
Luck! Well, call it that if you like. Call it luck if it makes
you feel any better. Only I happen to know differently.

Happens it happened to me—*and I know*. It isn't that I don't believe in luck. No, but it isn't what I mean. Say I was born innocent—that comes nearer to hitting the mark. When I think back to what I was as a kid, a kid of five or six, I realize that I haven't altered a bit. I'm just as pure and innocent as ever. I remember my first impression of the world—that it was good, *but terrifying*. It still looks that way to me—good but terrifying. It was easy to frighten me, but I never spoiled inside. You can frighten me to-day, but you can't make me sour. It's settled. It's in the blood.

I'm sitting down now to write a letter for Max. I'm writing to a woman in New York, a woman connected with a Jewish newspaper. I'm asking her to try to locate Max's sister in Coney Island. The last address was 156th Street near Broadway. *"And the name, Max?"* She had two names, his sister. Sometimes she called herself Mrs. Fischer, sometimes it was Mrs. Goldberg. "And you can't remember the house—whether it was on a corner or in the middle of the block?" No, he can't. He's lying now and I know it, but what the hell. Supposing there was no sister, what of it? There's something fishy about his story, but that's his affair, not mine.

It's even fishier, what he's doing now. He's pulling out a photograph taken when he was seven or eight—a photograph of mother and son. The photograph almost knocks the pins from under me. His mother is a *beautiful* woman —in the photograph. Max is standing stiffly by her side, a little frightened, the eyes wide open, his hair carefully parted, his little jacket buttoned up to the neck. They're standing somewhere near Lemberg, near the big fortress. The whole tragedy of the race is in the mother's face. A few years and Max too will have the same expression. Each new infant begins with a bright, innocent expression, the strong purity of the race moistening the large, dark eyes. They stand like that for several years and then suddenly, around puberty often, the expression changes. Suddenly they get up on their hind legs and they walk the tread-mill. The hair falls out, the teeth rot, the spine twists. Corns, bunions, calluses. The hand always sweating, the lips twitching. The head down, almost in the plate, and the food sucked in with big, swishing gulps. To think that they all started clean, with fresh diapers every day . . .

We're putting the photograph in the letter, as an identification. I'm asking Max to add a few words, in Yiddish, in that broomstick scrawl. He reads back to me what he has written and somehow I don't believe a word of it. We made a bundle of the suit and the dirty linen. Max is worried about the bundle—it's wrapped in newspaper and there's no string around it. He says he doesn't want to be seen going back to the hotel with that awkward looking bundle. He wants to look respectable. All the while he's fussing with the bundle he's thanking me profusely. He makes me feel as if I hadn't given him enough. Suddenly it occurs to me that there was a hat left here, a better one than the thing he's got on. I get it out and try it on. I show him how the hat should be worn. "You've got to turn the brim down and pull it well over your eye, see? And crush it in a bit—like that!" Max says it looks fine on me. I'm sorry I'm giving it away. Now Max tries it on, and as he puts it on I notice that he doesn't seem enthusiastic about it. He seems to be debating whether it's worth the trouble to take along. That settles it for me. I take him to the bathroom and I set it rakishly over his right eye. I crush the crown in even more rakishly. I know that makes him feel like a pimp or a gambler. Now I try the other hat on him —his own hat with the stiffly curled brim. I can see that he prefers that, silly as it looks. So I begin to praise the shit out of it. I tell him it becomes him more than the other. I talk him out of the other hat. And while he's admiring himself in the mirror I open the bundle and I extract a shirt and a couple of handkerchiefs and stuff them back in the drawer. Then I take him to the grocer at the corner and I have the woman wrap the bundle properly. He doesn't even thank the woman for her pains. He says she can afford to do me a service since I buy all my groceries from her.

We get off at the Place St. Michel. We walk towards his hotel in the Rue de la Harpe. It's the hour before dark when the walls glow with a soft, milky whiteness. I feel at peace with the world. It's the hour when Paris produces almost the effect of music upon one. Each stop brings to the eye a new and surprising architectural order. The houses actually seem to arrange themselves in musical notation: they suggest quaint minuets, waltzes, mazurkas, nocturnes. We are going into the oldest of the old, towards St. Severin and the narrow, twisting streets familiar to Dante and da Vinci. I'm trying to tell Max what a wonderful neighborhood he inhabits, what venerable associations are here stored away. I'm telling him about his predecessors, Dante and da Vinci.

"And when was all this?" he asks.

"Oh, around the 14th century," I answer.

"That's it," says Max, "before that it was no good and after that it has been no good. It was good in the 14th century and that's all." If I like it so well he'd be glad to change places with me.

We climb the stairs to his little room on the top floor. The stairs are carpeted to the third floor and above that they are waxed and slippery. On each floor is an enamel sign warning the tenants that cooking and washing are not permitted in the rooms. On each floor is a sign pointing to the water closet. Climbing the stairs you can look into the windows of the hotel adjoining; the walls are so close that if you stuck your mitt out the window you could shake hands with the tenants next door.

The room is small but clean. There's running water and a little commode in the corner. On the wall a few clothes hooks have been nailed up. Over the bed a yellow bulb. Thirty-seven francs a week. Not bad. He could have another for twenty-eight francs, but no running water. While he's complaining about the size of the room I step to the window and look out. There, almost touching me, is a young woman leaning out of the window. She's staring blankly at the wall opposite where the windows end. She seems to be in a trance. At her elbow are some tiny flowerpots; below the window, on an iron hook, hangs a dishrag. She seems oblivious of the fact that I'm standing at her side watching her. Her room, probably no larger than the one we're standing in, seems nevertheless to have brought her peace. She's waiting for it to get dark in order to slip down into the street. She probably doesn't know anything about her distinguished predecessors either, but the past is in her blood and she connects more easily with the lugubrious present. With the darkness coming on and my blood astir I get an almost holy feeling about this room I'm standing in. Perhaps to-night when I leave him Max will spread my book on the pillow and pore over it with heavy eyes. On the flyleaf it is written: "to my friend Max, the only man in Paris who really knows what suffering is." I had the feeling, as I inscribed these words, that my book was embarking on a strange adventure. I was thinking not so much of Max as of others unknown to me who would read these lines and wonder. I saw the book lying by the Seine, the pages torn and thumb-marked, passages underlined here and there, figures in the margin, coffee stains, a man with a big overcoat shoving it in his pocket, a voyage, a strange land, a man under the Equator writing me a letter: I saw it lying under a glass and the auctioneer's hammer coming down with a bang. Centuries passing and the face of the world changing, changing. And then again two men standing in a little room just like this, perhaps this very room, and next door a young woman leaning out of the window, the flower-pots at her elbow, the dish-rag hanging from the iron hook. And just as now one of the men is worn to death; his little room is a prison and the night gives him no comfort, no hope of relief. Weary and disheartened he holds the book which the other has given him. But he can take no courage from the book. He will toss on his bed in anguish and the nights will roll over him like the plague. He will have to die first in order to see the dawn . . . Standing in this room by the side of the man who is beyond all help my knowledge of the world and of men and women speaks cruelly and silently. Nothing but death will assuage this man's grief. There is nothing to do, as Boris says. It is all useless.

As we step into the hall again the lights go out. It seems to me as if Max were swallowed up in everlasting darkness.

It's not quite so dark outdoors though the lights are on everywhere. The Rue de la Harpe is thrumming. At the corner they are putting up an awning; there is a ladder standing in the middle of the street and a workman in big baggy trousers is sitting on top of it waiting for his sidekick to hand him a monkey-wrench or something. Across the street from the hotel is a little Greek restaurant with big terra cotta vases in the window. The whole street is theatrical. Everybody is poor and diseased and beneath our feet are catacombs choked with human bones. We take a turn around the block. Max is trying to pick out a suitable restaurant; he wants to eat in a *prix fixe* at 5.50 frs. When I make a face he points to a de luxe restaurant at 18 francs the meal. Clearly he's bewildered. He's lost all sense of values.

We go back to the Greek restaurant and study the menu pasted on the window. Max is afraid it's too high. I take a look inside and I see that it's crowded with whores and workmen. The men have their hats on, the floor is covered with sawdust, the lights are dingy. It's the sort of place where you might really have a good meal. I take Max by the arm and start dragging him in. A whore is just sailing out with a toothpick in her mouth. At the curb her companion is waiting for her; they walk down the street towards St. Severin, perhaps to drop in at the *bal musette* opposite the church. Dante must have dropped in there too once in a while—for a drink, what I mean. The whole Middle Ages is hanging there outside the door of the restaurant; I've got one foot in and one foot out. Max has already seated himself and is studying the menu. His bald head glistens under the yellow light. In the 14th century he would have been a mason or a joiner: I can see him standing on a scaffold with a trowel in his hand.

The place is filled with Greeks: the waiters are Greek, the proprietors are Greek, the food is Greek and the language is Greek. I want egg-plant wrapped in vine leaves, a nice patty of egg-plant swimming in lamb sauce, as only the Greeks know how to make it. Max doesn't care what he eats. He's afraid it's going to be too expensive for me. My idea is to duck Max as soon as the meal is over and take a stroll through the neighborhood. I'll tell him I have work to do—that always impresses him.

It's in the midst of the meal that Max suddenly opens up. I don't know what's brought it on. But suddenly he's talking a blue streak. As near as I can recall now he was visiting a French lady when suddenly, for no reason at all, he burst out crying. Such crying! He couldn't stop. He put his head down on the table and wept and wept, just like a broken-hearted child. The French lady was so disturbed that she wanted to send for a doctor. He was ashamed of himself. Ah yes, he remembers now what brought it about. He was visiting her and he was very hungry. It was near dinner time and suddenly he couldn't hold back any longer —he just up and asked her for a few francs. To his amazement she gave him the money immediately. A French lady! Then suddenly he felt miserable. To think that a strong, healthy fellow like himself should be begging a poor French lady for a few sous. Where was his pride? What would become of him if he had to beg from a woman?

That was how it began. Thinking about it the tears came to his eyes. The next moment he was sobbing, then, just as with the French lady, he put his head on the table and he wept. It was horrible.

"You could stick a dagger into me," he said, when he had calmed himself, "you could do anything to me, but you could never make me cry. Now I cry for no reason at all—it comes over me like that, all of a sudden, and I can't stop it."

He asks me if I think he's a neurasthenic. He was told it was just a *crise de nerfs. That's a breakdown, isn't it?* He remembers the dentist again, his saying right away it's nothing, just nervousness. How could the dentist tell that? He's afraid it's the beginning of something worse. Is he going mad perhaps? He wants to know the truth.

What the hell can I tell him? I tell him it's nothing—just nerves.

"That doesn't mean you're going buggy," I add. "It'll pass soon as you get on your feet . . ."

"But I shouldn't be alone so much, Miller!"

Ah, that makes me wary. I know what's coming now. I ought to drop in on him oftener. Not money! No, he underlines that continually. But that he shouldn't be alone so much!

"Don't worry, Max. We're coming down often, Boris and I. We're going to show you some good times."

He doesn't seem to be listening.

"Sometimes, Miller, when I go back to my room, the sweat begins to run down my face. I don't know what it is . . . it's like I had a mask on."

"That's because you're worried, Max. It's nothing . . . You drink a lot of water too, don't you?"

He nods his head instantly, and then looks at me rather terrified.

"How did you know that?" he asks. "How is it I'm so thirsty all the time? All day long I'm running to the hydrant. I don't know what's the matter with me . . . *Miller, I want to ask you something:* is it true what they say, that if you're taken sick here they do you in? I was told that if you're a foreigner and you have no money they do away with you. I'm thinking about it all day long. What if I should be taken sick? I hope to God I shouldn't lose my mind. *I'm afraid, Miller* . . . I've heard such terrible stories about the French. You know how they are . . . you know they'll let you die before their eyes. They have no heart! It's always money, money, money. God help me, Miller, if I should ever fall so low as to beg them for mercy! Now at least I have my *carte d'identité*. A *tourist* they made me! Such bastards! How do they expect a man to live? Sometimes I sit and I look at the people passing by. Every one seems to have something to do, except me. I ask myself sometimes—*Max, what is wrong with you?* Why should I be obliged to sit all day and do nothing? It's eating me up. In the busy season, when there's a little work, I'm the first man they send for. They know that Max is a good presser. *The French!* what do they know about pressing? Max had to show them how to press. Two francs an hour they give me, because I have no right to work. That's how they take advantage of a white man in this lousy country. They make out of him a bum!"

He pauses a minute. "You were saying, Miller, about South America, that maybe I could start all over again and bring myself to my feet again. I'm not an old man yet— only *morally* I'm defeated. Twenty years now I've been pressing. Soon I'll be too old . . . my career is finished. Yes, if I could do some light work, something where I shouldn't have to use my hands . . . That's why I wanted to become an *interprète*. After you hold an iron for twenty years your fingers aren't so nimble any more. I feel disgusted with myself when I think of it. All day standing over a hot iron . . . the smell of it! Sometimes when I think on

t I feel I must vomit. Is it right that a man should stand
ll day over a hot iron? Why then did God give us the
grass and the trees? Hasn't Max a right to enjoy that too?
Must we be slaves all our lives—just to make money,
money, money . . . ?"

On the *terrasse* of a café, after we've had our coffee, I
manage to break away from him. Nothing is settled, except
that I've promised to keep in touch with him. I walk along
the Boulevard St. Michel past the Jardin du Luxembourg.
I suppose he's sitting there where I left him. I told him to
stay there awhile instead of going back to the room. I know
he won't sit there very long. Probably he's up already and
doing the rounds. It's better that way too—better to go
round bumming a few sous than to sit doing nothing. It's
summer now and there are some Americans in town. The
trouble is they haven't much money to spend. It's not like
'27 and '8 when they were lousy with dough. Now they
expect to have a good time on fifty francs.

Up near the Observatoire it's quiet as the grave. Near a
broken wall a lone whore is standing listlessly, too dis-
couraged even to make a sign. At her feet is a mass of litter
—dead leaves, old newspapers, tin cans, brushwood, cigarette stubs. She looks as though she were ready to flop
there, right in the dung heap, and call it a day.

Walking along the Rue St. Jacques the whole thing gets
confused in my mind. The Rue St. Jacques is just one long
picturesque shit-house. In every wormy little shack a radio.
It's hallucinating to hear these crooning American voices
coming out of the dark holes on either side of me. It's like
a combination of five-and-ten-cent store and Middle Ages.
A war veteran is wheeling himself along in a wheel chair,
his crutches at his side. Behind him a big limousine waiting
for a clearance in order to go full speed ahead. From the
radios, all hitched up to the same station, comes that sick-
ening American air—"*I believe in miracles!*" Miracles!
Miracles! Jesus, even Christ Almighty couldn't perform a
miracle here! *Eat, drink, this is my body broken for thee!*
In the windows of the religious shops are inexpensive
crosses to commemorate the event. A poor Jew nailed to
a cross so that we might have life everlasting. And haven't
we got it though . . . cement and balloon tires and radios

and loud-speakers and whores with wooden legs and com
modities in such abundance that there's no work for the
starving . . . *I'm afraid that I should be alone too much*
On the sixth floor, when he enters his room, the sweat begins to roll down his face—*as if he had a mask on!* Nothing
could make me cry, not even if you stuck a dagger in me—
but now I cry for nothing! I cry and cry and I can't stop
myself. *Do you think, Miller, I am going mad?* Is he going
mad? Jesus, Max, all I can tell you is that the whole world's
going mad. You're mad, I'm mad, everybody's mad. The
whole world's busting with pus and sorrow. Have you
wound your watch up? Yes, I know you still carry one—
I saw it sticking out of your vest pocket. No matter how
bad it gets you want to know what time it is. I'll tell you,
Max, what time it is—to the split second. *It's just five
minutes before the end.* When it comes midnight on the
dot that will be the end. Then you can go down into the
street and throw your clothes away. Everybody will pop
into the street new-born. That's why they were putting up
the awning this evening. They were getting ready for the
miracle. And the young woman leaning out of the window,
you remember? She was dreaming of the dawn, of how
lovely she would look when she would come down amidst
the throng *and they would see her in the flesh.*

MIDNIGHT

Nothing has happened.

8:00 A.M. It's raining. A day just like any other day.

Noon. The postman arrives with a pneumatique. The
scrawl looks familiar. I open it. It's from Max, as I
thought . . .

"To My Dear friends Miller and Boris—I am writing
to you these few lines having got up from bed and it is
3 o'clock in the morning I cannot sleep, am very nervis, I
am crying and cant stop, I hear music playing in my ears,
but in reality I hear screaming in the street, I suppose a
pimp must have beaten up his hur—it is a terrible noise,
I cant stand it, the water tape is running in the sink, I cant
do a wink of sleep I am reading your book Miller in order
to quieten me, its amusing me but I have no patience I am

waiting for the morning I'll get out in the street as soon as daylight breaks. A long night of suffering though I am not very hungary but I am afraid of something I don't know what is the matter with me—I talk to myself I cant control myself. Miller, I don't want you to help me any more. I want to talk to you, am I a child? I have no courage, am I losing my reason? Dear Miller really don't think I need you for money, I want to talk to you and to Boris, no money, only moral help I need. I am afraid of my room I am afraid to sleep alone—is it the end of my carrier? It seems to me. I have played the last cart. I cant breed. I want morning to come to get out in the street. I am praying to God to help me to pass quigly this terrible night, yes it is a night of agony. I cant stand the heat, and the atmosphere of my room. I am not drunk believe me while I'm writing this—only I pass the time away and it seems to me that I'm speaking to you and so I am finding a little comfort but I am afraid to be alone—what is it, it is just raining outside and I'm looking out of the window, that does me good, the rain is talking to me but morning wont come—it seems to me that night will never end. I am afraid the french will do me away in case of sickness because being a forinner is that so? Miller, tell me is it true—I was told that if a forinner is sick and has nobody they do him away quickly instead of curing him even when there is a chance. I am afraid the french shouldn't take me away, then I shall never see daylight. Oh no, I shall be brave and control myself but I don't want to go out in the street now, the Police might take a false statement, else I should go out now of my Room out in the street, for I cant stay in my Room, but I'm much afraid every night, I'm afraid. Dear Miller, is it possible to see you? I want to talk to you a little. I don't want no money, I'm going crazy. Sincerely yours, Max."

RIDER HAGGARD

SINCE MENTIONING Rider Haggard's name, his book, *She*, has fallen into my hands. I have now read about two-thirds of it, my first glance at the book since the year 1905 or 1906, as best I remember. I feel impelled to relate, as quietly and restrained as I can, the extraordinary reactions which I am now experiencing as a result of this second reading. To begin with, I must confess that not until I came to Chapter II, "The Plain of Kôr," did I have the faintest recollection of reading a word of this startling book before. I was certain, nevertheless, that the moment I encountered that mysterious creature called Ayesha (She) my memory would come alive. It has fallen out just as I anticipated. As with *The Lion of the North,* referred to earlier, so in *She* I rediscover the emotions which first overcame me upon coming face to face with a "femme fatale." (*The* femme fatale!) Ayesha, the true name of this ageless beauty,* this lost soul who refuses to die until her beloved returns to earth again, occupies a position—at least, in my mind— comparable to the Sun in the galaxy of immortal lovers, all of them cursed with a deathless beauty. In this starry firmament Helen of Troy is but a pale moon. Indeed, and only today can I say it with certitude, Helen was never real to me. Ayesha is more than real. She is super-real, in every sense of that maligned word. About her personage the author has spun a web of such proportions that it almost deserves the appellation "cosmogonic." Helen is legendary,

---

* Also the name of Mahomet's second and favorite wife.

mythical—*de la littérature*. Ayesha is of the eternal elements, both discarnate and incarnate. She is of the dark mothers, of which mysterious race we get hints and echoes in Germanic literature. But before I babble on about the wonders of this narrative, which dates from the next to the last decade of the Nineteenth Century, let me speak of certain revelations concerning my own character and identity which are connected with it.

As I write this book I keep jotting down the titles of books I have read, as they return to memory. It is a game which has taken complete possession of me. The reasons for it I have already begun to perceive. The primary one is that I am rediscovering my own identity which, unknown to me, had been smothered or stifled in the pages of certain books. That is to say, in finding myself, through certain authors who acted as my intermediaries, I had also (without knowing it) lost myself. And this must have happened over and over again. For, what happens to me every day now is this: the mere recollection of a forgotten title brings to life not only the aura of the book's untouchable personality but the knowledge and the reality of my former selves. I need not add that something approaching awe, dread, consternation is beginning to take hold of me. I am coming to grips with myself in a wholly new and unexpected way. It is almost as if I were embarked on that journey to Tibet I have so frequently alluded to and which I have less and less need to make as times goes on and I myself go on, crab-wise, as seems to be my destiny.

Not for naught, I perceive more and more profoundly, have I clung to childhood memories; not for naught have I attached such importance to "the boys in the street," our life together, our gropings for truth, our struggle to understand the perverse order of society in which we found ourselves enmeshed and from whose grip we vainly sought to free ourselves.

Just as there are two orders of human knowledge, two kinds of wisdom, two traditions, two everything, so in boyhood we came to realize that there were two sources of instruction: the one which we discovered ourselves and secretly strove to guard, and the other which we learned about in school and which impressed us as not only dull and futile, but diabolically false and perverted. The one kind of instruction nourished us, the other undermined us. And I mean this "literally and in every sense," to use Rimbaud's expression.

Every genuine boy is a rebel and an anarch. If he were allowed to develop according to his own instincts, his own inclinations, society would undergo such a radical transformation as to make the adult revolutionary cower and cringe. His would probably not be a comfortable or benevolent pattern of organization, but it would reflect justice, splendor and integrity. It would accelerate the vital pulse of life, abet and augment life. And what could be more terrifying to adults than such a prospect.

"A bas l'histoire!" (Rimbaud's words.) Do you begin to see the pregnancy of them?

The books which we recommended to one another on the q.t., the books which we devoured stealthily at all hours of the day and night—and in the weirdest places sometimes! —these books which we discussed in the empty lot, or on a street corner under an arc light, or at the edge of a cemetery, or in an icehouse of our own construction or a cave dug into a hillside, or in any secret place of gathering, for we always met as a clan, as blood brothers, as members of a secret order—The Order of Youth Defending the Traditions of Youth!—these books were part of our daily instruction, part of our Spartan discipline and our spiritual training. They were the heritage of anterior orders, inconspicuous groups like ourselves, who from earliest times fought to keep alive and to prolong, if possible, the golden age of youth. We were not aware then that our elders, some of them at least, looked back on this hallowed period of their lives with envy and longing; we had no suspicion that our glorious dynasty would be referred to as "the period of conflict." We did not know that we were little primitives, or archaic heroes, saints, martyrs, gods or demigods. *We knew that we were*—and that was sufficient. We wanted a voice in the government of our affairs: we did not want to be treated as embryonic adults. For most of us, neither father nor mother were objects of veneration, much less of idolatry. We opposed their dubious authority as best we could—and at great odds, it goes without saying. Our law, and it was the only voice of authority we truly respected, was the law of life. That we understood this law was revealed by the games we played, that is, by the way we played them and the inferences we drew from the way the various players entered into them. We established genuine hierarchies; we passed judgment according to our various levels of understanding, our various levels of being. We were conscious of the peak as well as of the base of the pyramid. We had faith, reverence and discipline. We created our own ordeals and tests of power and fitness. We abided by the decisions of our superiors, or our chief. He was king who manifested the dignity and the power of his rank—and he never ruled a day beyond his time!

I speak of these facts with some emotion because it amazes me that adults should ever forget them, as I see they do. We all experience a thrill when, having put the past behind us, we suddenly find ourselves among the "primitives." I mean now the true primitive: early man. The study of anthropology has one great merit—it permits us to live again as youths. The true student of primitive peoples has respect, deep respect, for these "ancestors" who exist side by side with us but who do not "grow up." He finds that man in the early stages of his development is in no wise inferior to man in the later stages; some have even found early man to be superior, in most respects, to late man. "Early" and "late" are here used according to the vulgar acceptation of the terms. We know nothing, in truth, about the origin of early man or whether, indeed, he was young or decadent. And we know little about the origin of "homo sapiens," though we pretend much. There is a gap between the farthest reaches of history and the relics and evidences of prehistoric man, branches of which such as the Cro-Magnon, baffle us by the evidences of their intelligence and aesthetic sensibility. The wonders which we constantly expect the archaeologist to unearth, the links in our very slender thread of knowledge about our own species, are supplied incessantly and in the most amazing ways by those whom we refer to condescendingly as "imaginative" writers. I limit myself to these latter for the moment since the others, sometimes termed "occult" or "esoteric" writers, are still less accredited. They are for "second childhood" (sic).

Rider Haggard is one of those imaginative writers who undoubtedly fed from many streams. We think of him now as a writer of boys' books, content to let his name fade into oblivion. Perhaps only when our scientific explorers and investigators stumble upon the truths revealed through imagination will we recognize the true stature of such a writer.

"What is imagination?" asks Rider Haggard in the midst of his narrative. And he answers: "Perhaps it is a shadow of the intangible truth, perhaps it is the soul's thought!"

It was in the imagination that Blake lived entirely. It was imagination which led a humble grocery boy (Schliemann), fired by his reading of Homer, to go in search of Troy, Tiryns and Mycenae. And what of Jacob Boehme? What of the intrepid Frenchman, Caillé, the first white man to enter Timbuctoo and come out alive? What an epic!

Curious, but just about the time that I first became acquainted with the mysteries of Egypt, the dazzling history of Crete, the bloody annals of the House of Atreus, just when I am overwhelmed by my first contact with such themes as reincarnation, split personality, the Holy Grail, resurrection and immortality, and so on, via such "romancers" as Herodotus, Tennyson, Scott, Sienkiewicz, Henty, Bulwer-Lytton, Marie Corelli, Robert Louis Stevenson and others, many others, all these so-called legends, myths and superstitious beliefs were beginning to take substance in fact. Schliemann, Sir Arthur Evans, Frazer, Frobenius, Annie Besant, Madame Blavatsky, Paul Radin, a whole flock of courageous pioneers had been busy unveiling the truth in one realm after another, all interlocked, all contributory in breaking the spell of defeat and paralysis in which the doctrines of the Nineteenth Century held us. The new century opens with promise and splendor; the past comes alive again, but tangibly, substantially, and with almost greater reality than the present.

When I stood amid the ruins of Knossos and of Mycenae did my thoughts turn to school books, to my penal instructors and the enchanting tales they told us? No. I thought of the stories I had read as a child; I saw the illustrations of those books I had thought buried in oblivion; I thought of our discussions in the street and the amazing speculations we had indulged in. I recalled my own private speculation about all these exciting, mysterious themes connected with past and future. Looking out over the plain of Argos from Mycenae, I lived over again—and how vividly!—the tale of the Argonauts. Gazing upon the Cyclopean walls of Tiryns I recalled the tiny illustration of the wall in one of my wonder books—it corresponded exactly with the reality confronting me. Never, in school, had a history professor even attempted to make living for us these glorious epochs of the past which every child enters into naturally as soon as he is able to read. With what childlike faith does the hardy explorer pursue his grim task! We learn nothing from the pedagogues. The true educators are the adventurers and wanderers, the men who plunge into the living plasm of history, legend, myth.

A moment ago I spoke of the world youth might create, if given a chance. I have noticed repeatedly how frightening to parents is the thought of educating a child according to their own private notions. As I write I recall a momentous scene connected with this subject which passed between the mother of my first child and myself. It was in the kitchen of our home, and it followed upon some heated words of mine about the futility and absurdity of sending the child to school. Thoroughly engrossed, I had gotten up from the table and was pacing back and forth in the little room. Suddenly I heard her ask, almost frantically: *"But where would you begin? How?"* So deep in thought was I that the full import of her words came to me *bien en retard*. Pacing back and forth, head down, I found myself up against the hall door just as her words penetrated my consciousness. And at that very moment my eyes came to rest on a small knot in the panel of the door. How would I begin? Where? *"Why there! Anywhere!"* I bellowed. And pointing to the knot in the wood I launched into a brilliant, devastating monologue that literally swept her off her feet. I must have carried on for a full half hour, hardly knowing what I was saying but swept along by a torrent of ideas long pent up. What gave it paprika, so to speak, was the exasperation and disgust which welled up with the recollection of my experiences in school. I began with that little knot of wood, how it came about, what it meant, and thence found myself treading, or rushing, through a veritable labyrinth of knowledge, instinct, wisdom, intuition and experience. Everything is so divinely connected, so beautifully interrelated—how could one possibly be at a loss to undertake the education of a child? Whatever we touch, see, smell or hear, from whatever point we begin, we are on velvet. It is like pushing buttons that open magical doors. It works by itself, creates its own traction and momentum. There is no need to "prepare" the child for his lesson: the lesson itself is a kind of enchantment. The child longs to know; he literally hungers and thirsts. And so does the adult, if we could but dissipate the hypnotic thrall which subjugates him.

To what lengths the teacher may go, to what heights he may rise, what powers he may draw on, we have but to turn to the story of Helen Keller's awakening to learn. There was a great teacher, this Miss Sullivan. A pupil deaf, dumb and blind—what a task to confront! The miracles she accomplished were born of love and patience. Patience, love, understanding. But above all, *patience*. Whoever has not read the amazing life of Helen Keller has missed one of the great chapters in the history of education.

When I came to read of Socrates and of the Peripatetic schools, when later in Paris I roamed through the precincts haunted by Dante (the university curricula were then conducted out of doors . . . there is a street in this district, near Notre Dame, named after the very straw they slept on, these ardent students of the Middle Ages), when I read of the origins of our postal system and the part played in it by university students (who were the runners), when I thought of that lifelike education I had unwittingly received in such places as Union Square and Madison Square, where the soapbox orators held forth, when I recalled the heroic *rôles,* which in truth were *educational* rôles, played by such figures of the public square as Elizabeth Gurley Flynn, Carlo Tresca, Giovanitti, Big Bill Haywood, Jim Larkin, Hubert Harrison and such like, I was more than ever convinced that as boys, *on our own,* we were on the right track: we had sensed that education was a *vital* process, one acquired in the midst of life by living and wrestling with life. I felt closer then to Plato, Pythagoras, Epictetus, Dante and all the ancient illustrious ones than ever before or since. When my Hindu messenger boys in the telegraph company told me of Tagore's famous "Shantiniketan," when I read of Ramakrishna's bright abode, when I thought of Saint Francis and the birds, I knew that the world was wrong and that education as it is conducted today is disastrous. We who have sat behind closed doors on hard benches in foul rooms under stern eyes, hostile eyes, we have been betrayed, stunted, martyrized. *A bas les écoles! Vive le plein air!* Once again, I say, I plan to read *Emile*. What matter if Rousseau's theories proved a fiasco? I shall read him as I read the works of Ferrer, Montessori, Pestalozzi and all the others. Anything to put a spike in our present system which turns out dolts, jackasses, tame ducks, weathervanes, bigots and blind leaders of the blind. If needs be, let us take to the jungle!

Behold the lot of man! Certainly it shall overtake us, and we shall sleep. Certainly, too, we shall awake and live again, and again shall sleep, and so on and so on, through periods, spaces, and times, from aeon unto aeon, till the world is dead, and the worlds beyond the world are dead, and naught liveth save the Spirit that is Life . . .

Thus speaks Ayesha in the tombs of Kôr.

A boy wonders mightily over such a phrase as the last— "and naught liveth save the Spirit that is Life." If he was sent to church as well as to school, he heard much about the Spirit from the pulpit. But from the pulpit such talk falls on deaf ears. It is only when one becomes awake—twenty, thirty, forty years later—that the words of the Gospel acquire depth and meaning. The Church is wholly unrelated to the other activities of a boy's life. All that remains of this discipline, this instruction, is the awesome, majestic sound of the English language when it was in flower. The rest is jumble and confusion. There is no initiation, such as the common "savage" receives. Nor can there be any spiritual blossoming. The world of the chapel and the world outside are distinct and utterly apart. The language and behavior of Jesus do not conform to sense until one has passed through sorrow and travail, until one has become desperate, lost, utterly forsaken and abandoned.

That there is something beyond, above, and anterior to earthly life, every boy instinctively divines. It is only a few years since he himself lived wholly in the Spirit. He has an identity which manifests itself at birth. He struggles to preserve this precious identity. He repeats the rituals of his primitive forbears, he relives the struggles and ordeals of mythical heroes, he organizes his own secret order—to preserve a sacred tradition. Neither parents, teachers nor preachers play any part in this all-important domain of youth. Looking back upon myself as a boy, I feel exactly like a member of the lost tribe of Israel. Some, like Alain-Fournier in *The Wanderer,* are never able to desert this secret order of youth. Bruised by every contact with the world of adults, they immolate themselves in dream and reverie. Especially in the realm of love are they made to suffer. Occasionally they leave us a little book, a testament of the true and ancient faith, which we read with dim eyes, marvelling over its sorcery, aware, but too late, that we are looking at ourselves, that we are weeping over our own fate.

More than ever do I believe that at a certain age it becomes imperative to reread the books of childhood and youth. Else we may go to the grave not knowing who we are or why we lived.

A stonyhearted mother is our earth, and stones are the bread she gives her children for their daily food. Stones to eat and bitter water for their thirst, and stripes for tender nurture.

A boy wonders if it be truly thus. Such thoughts fill him with anguish and dismay. He wonders again when he reads that "out of good cometh evil and out of evil good." Familiar though it be, coming from the mouth of Ayesha the thought troubles him. Of such matters he has heard little that was not mere echo. He surmises that he is indeed in some mysterious fane.

But it is when Ayesha explains that it is not by force but by terror that she reigns, when she exclaims—*"My empire is of the imagination"*—it is then a boy is startled to the core. *The imagination?* He has not heard yet of "the undenominated legislators of the world." Well he has not. There is a mightier thought here, something which lifts us above the world and all question of dominion over it. There is the hint—at least for a boy!—that if man only dared to *imagine* the dazzling possibilities life offers he would realize them to the full. There creeps over him a suspicion, even if fleeting, that age, death, evil, sin, ugliness, crime and frustration are but limitations conceived by man and imposed by man upon himself and his fellow man . . . In this fleeting moment one is shaken to the roots. One begins to question everything. The result, needless to say, is that he is covered with mockery and ridicule. "Thou art foolish, my son!" That is the refrain.

There will come similar confrontations with the written word, more and more of them, as time goes on. Some will be even more shattering, more impenetrable. Some will send him reeling to the brink of madness. And ever and always none to offer a helping hand. No, the farther one advances the more one stands alone. One becomes like a naked infant abandoned in the wilderness. Finally one runs amok or one conforms. At this juncture the drama surrounding one's "identity" is played out for good and all. At this point the die is cast irrevocably. One joins up—or one takes to the jungle. From boy to wage earner, husband, father, then judge—it all seems to take place in the twinkle of an eye. One does one's best—that age-old excuse. Meanwhile life passes us by. Our backs ever bent to receive the lash, we have only to murmur a few words of gratitude and our persecutors accept our reverence. Only one hope remains—to become oneself tyrant and executioner. From "The Place of Life," where one took his stance as a boy, one passes over into the Tomb of Death, the only death which man has a right to avoid and evade: *living death*.

"There is one being, one law and one faith, as there is only one race of man," says Eliphas Levi in his celebrated work, *The History of Magic*.

I would not be rash enough to say that a boy understands such a statement but I will say that he is much nearer to understanding it than the so-called "wise" adult. The boy prodigy, Arthur Rimbaud—that sphinx of modern literature—we have reason to believe was obsessed by this idea. In a study devoted to him* I dubbed him "The Columbus of Youth." I felt that he had preempted this domain. Because of his refusal to surrender the vision of truth which he had glimpsed as a mere boy he turned his back on poetry, broke with his confrères, and, in accepting a life of brute toil, literally committed suicide. In the hell of Aden he asks: *"What am I doing here?"* In the famous *Lettre d'un Voyant* we have intimations of a thought which Levi has expressed thus: "It may be understood in a day to come that seeing is actually speaking and that the consciousness of light is a twilight of eternal life in being." It is in this singular twilight that many boys live their days. Is it any wonder then that certain books, originally intended for adults, should be appropriated by boys?

Speaking of the Devil, Levi says: "We would point out that whatsoever has a name exists; speech may be uttered in vain, but in itself it cannot be vain, and it has a meaning invariably." The ordinary adult finds it difficult to accept such a statement. Even the writer, particularly the "cultured" writer, for whom presumably the "word" is sacred, finds this thought unpalatable. A boy, on the other hand, if such a statement were explained to him, would find truth and meaning in it. For him nothing is "in vain;" neither is anything too incredible, too monstrous, for him to swallow. Our children are at home in a world which seems to terrify and stupefy us. I am not thinking altogether of the sadistic trend which has come to the fore; I am thinking rather of the unknown worlds, microcosmic and macrocosmic, whose impingement on our own quaking world of feeble reality has now become oppressive and menacing. Our grown-up boys, the scientists, prate about the imminent conquest of the moon; our children have already voyaged far beyond the moon. They are ready, at a moment's notice, to take off for Vega—and beyond. They beg our supposedly superior intellects to furnish them with a new cosmogony and a new cosmology. They have grown intolerant of our naïve, limited, antiquated theories of the universe.

If Rimbaud may be said to have broken his heart with

* *The Time of the Assassins* (New Directions, New York).

chagrin because of his failure to win his contemporaries over to a new—*and truly modern*—view of man, if he surrendered all desire to establish a new heaven and a new earth, we now know why. The time was not ripe. Nor is it yet, apparently. (Though we should beware more and more of all "seeming" obstacles, hindrances and barriers.) The rhythm of time has been accelerated almost beyond comprehension. We are moving towards the day, and with frightening speed, when past, present and future will appear as one. The millennium ahead will not resemble, in duration, any like period in the past. It may be like the wink of an eye.

But to return to *She* . . . The chapter in which Ayesha is consumed in the flame of life—an extraordinary piece of writing!—is burned into my being. It was at this point in the narrative that I came awake—and remembered. It was because of this gruesome, harrowing event that the book remained with me all these years. That I had difficulty in summoning it from the depths of memory I attribute to the naked horror which it inspired. In the brief space which Haggard takes to describe her death one lives through the whole gamut of devolution. It is not death indeed which he describes but reduction. One is privileged, as it were, to assist at the spectacle of Nature reclaiming from her victim the secret which had been stolen from her. By observing the process in reverse the sense of awe which lies at the very roots of our being is enhanced. Prepared to witness a miracle, we are made to participate in a fiasco beyond human comprehension. It is at the Place of Life, let me remind the reader, that this unique death takes place. Life and death, Haggard tells us, are very close together. What he probably meant us to understand is that they are twins, and that only once is it given us to experience the miracle of life, only once the miracle of death: what happens in between is like the turning of a wheel, a perpetual rotation about an inner void, a dream that never ends, the activity of the wheel having nothing to do with the movement engendering it.

The deathless beauty of Ayesha, her seeming immortality, her wisdom which is ageless, her powers of sorcery and enchantment, her dominion over life and death, as

Rider Haggard slowly but deftly reveals this mysterious being to us, might well serve as a description of the soul of Nature. That which sustains Ayesha, and at the same time consumes her, is the faith that she will eventually be reunited with her beloved. And what could the Beloved be but the holy Spirit? No less a gift than this could suffice a soul endowed with her matchless hunger, patience and fortitude. The love which alone can transform the soul of Nature is divine love. Time counts for naught when spirit and soul are divorced. The splendor of neither can be made manifest except through union. Man, the only creature possessed of a dual nature, remains a riddle unto himself, keeps revolving on the wheel of life and death, until he pierces the enigma of identity. The drama of love, which is the highest he may enact, carries within it the key to the mystery. One law, one being, one faith, one race of man. Aye! "To die means to be cut off, not to cease being." In his inability to surrender to life, man cuts himself off. Ayesha, seemingly deathless, had thus cut herself off by renouncing the spirit which was in her. The beloved Kallikrates, her twin soul, unable to bear the splendor of her soul when he gazes upon it for the first time, is killed by Ayesha's own will. The punishment for this incestuous murder is arrestation. Ayesha, invested with beauty, power, wisdom and youth, is doomed to wait until her Beloved assumes flesh once again. The generations of time which pass in the interval are like the period separating one incarnation from another. Ayesha's Devachan is the Caves of Kôr. There she is as remote from life as the soul in limbo. In this same dread place Kallikrates too, or rather the preserved shell of her immortal love, passes the interval. His image is with her constantly. Possessive in life, Ayesha is equally possessive in death. Jealousy, manifesting itself in a tyrannical will, in an insatiable love of power, burns in her with the brightness of a funeral pyre. She has all time, seemingly, in which to review her past, to weigh her deeds, her thoughts, her emotions. An endless time of preparation for the one lesson she has yet to learn—the lesson of love. Godlike, she is yet more vulnerable than the merest mortal. Her faith is born of despair, not of love, not of understanding. It is a faith which will be tested in cruelest fashion. The veil which wraps her round, the veil which no mortal man has penetrated—her divine virginity, in short—will be removed, torn from her, at the crucial moment. Then she will stand revealed to herself. Then, open to love, she will move forward in spirit as well as soul. Then she will be ready for the miracle of death, that death which comes but once. With the coming of this final death she will enter the deathless realm of being. Isis, to whom she had sworn eternal devotion, will be no more. Devotion, transformed by love, merges with understanding, then death, then divine being. That which always was, always will be, now is eternally. Nameless, timeless, indefinable, the nature of one's true identity is thus swallowed up in the manner of the dragon swallowing its tail.

To summarize thus briefly the salient features of this great romance, especially perhaps to offer interpretation of his theme, is to do an injustice to the author. But there is a duality in Rider Haggard which intrigues me enormously. An earth-bound individual, conventional in his ways, orthodox in his beliefs, though full of curiosity and tolerance, endowed with great vitality and practical wisdom, this man who is reticent and reserved, English to the core, one might say, reveals through his "romances" a hidden nature, a hidden being, a hidden lore which is amazing. His method of writing these romances—at full speed, hardly stopping to think, so to speak—enabled him to tap his unconscious with freedom and depth. It is as if, by virtue of this technique, he found the way to project the living plasm of previous incarnations. In spinning his tales he permits the narrator to philosophize in a loose way, thus permitting the reader to obtain glimpses and flashes of his true thoughts. His story-teller's gift, however, is too great for him to allow his deepest reflections to assume the cloying form and dimensions which would break the spell of the recital.

With these brief sidelights on the author for the reader who may not know *She* or the sequel called *Ayesha,* let me proceed to expose some of the mysterious filaments by which a boy, this particular boy, myself, was bound and doubtless formed in ways beyond his knowing. I have said that Helen of Troy was never real to me. Certainly I read of her before I happened upon *She*. Everything relating to the golden legends of Troy and Crete was part of my childhood legacy. Through the tales interwoven with the legend and romance of King Arthur and his Knights of the Round Table I had become acquainted with other legendary and deathless beauties, notably Isolt. The awesome deeds of Merlin and other hoary wizards were also familiar to me. I had presumably steeped myself in tales dealing with the rites of the dead, as practiced in Egypt and elsewhere. I mention all this to indicate that the collision with Rider Haggard's subject matter was not in the nature of a first shock. I had been prepared, if I may put it that way. But perhaps because of his skill as a narrator, perhaps because he had struck just the right tone, the right level of understanding for a boy, the force of these combined factors permitted the arrow to reach its destined target for the first time. I was pierced through and through—in the Place of Love, in the Place of Beauty, in the Place of Life. It was in the Place of Life that I received the mortal wound. Just as Ayesha had dealt death to her beloved instead of life, thereby condemning herself to a prolonged purgatorial existence, so had I been dealt a "little" death, I suspect, on closing this book some forty-five years ago. Gone, seemingly forever, were my visions of Love, of Eternal Beauty, of Renunciation and Sacrifice, of Life Eternal. Like Rimbaud, however, in referring to the visions of the poet-seer, I may exclaim: *"But I saw them!"* Ayesha, consumed by the devouring flame, at the very source and fount of life, took with her into limbo all that was sacred and precious to me. *Only once is it given to experience the miracle of life.* The import of this dawns slowly, very slowly, upon me. Again and again I revolt against books, against raw experience, against wisdom itself, as well as Nature and God knows what all. But I am always brought back, sometimes at the very edge of the fateful precipice.

"Whoever has not become fully alive in this life will not become so through death."* I believe this to be the hidden note in all religious teachings. "To die," as Gutkind says, "means to be *cut off,* not to cease." Cut off from what?

* *The Absolute Collective,* by Erich Gutkind.

From everything: from love, participation, wisdom, experience, but above all, from the very source of life.

Youth is one kind of aliveness. It is not the only kind, but it is vitally linked to the world of spirit. To worship youth instead of life itself is as disastrous as to worship power. Only wisdom is eternally renewable. But of life-wisdom contemporary man knows little. He has not only lost his youth, he has lost his innocence. He clings to illusions, ideals, beliefs.

In the chapter called "What We Saw," which affects me as deeply now as it did long ago, the narrator, after watching Ayesha consumed by the flame of life, reflects thus: "Ayesha locked up in her living tomb, waiting from age to age for the coming of her lover, worked but a small change in the order of the world. But Ayesha, strong and happy in her love, clothed with immortal youth, godlike beauty and power, and the wisdom of the centuries, would have revolutionized society, and even perchance have changed the destinies of Mankind." And then he adds this sentence, upon which I have pondered long: "Thus she opposed herself to the eternal law, and, strong though she was, by it was swept back into nothingness . . ."

One immediately thinks of the great figures in myth, legend and history who attempted to revolutionize society and thereby alter the destiny of man: Lucifer, Prometheus, Akhnaton, Ashoka, Jesus, Mahomet, Napoleon . . . One thinks especially of Lucifer, the Prince of Darkness, the most shining revolutionary of all. Each one paid for his "crime." Yet all are revered. The rebel, I firmly believe, is closer to God than the saint. To him is given dominion over the dark forces which we must obey before we can receive the light of illumination. The return to the source, the only revolution which has meaning for man, is the whole goal of man. It is a revolution which can occur only in his being. This is the true significance of the plunge into life's stream, of becoming fully alive, awakening, recovering one's complete identity.

Identity! This is the word which, on rereading Rider Haggard has come to haunt me. It is the riddle of identity which caused such books as *Louis Lambert, Seraphita, Interlinear to Cabeza de Vaca, Siddhartha,* to exercise dominion over me. I began my writing career with the intention of telling the truth about myself. What a fatuous task! What can possibly be more fictive than the story of one's life? "We learn nothing by reading [Winckelman]," said Goethe, "we *become* something." Similiarly I might say—we reveal nothing of ourselves by telling the truth, but we do sometimes *discover* ourselves. I who had thought to *give* something found that I had *received* something.

Why the emphasis, in my works, on crude repetitious experience of life? Is it not dust in the eye? Am I revealing myself or finding myself? In the world of sex I seem alternately to lose and to find myself. It is all seeming. The conflict, which if not hidden is certainly smothered, is the conflict between Spirit and Reality. (*Spirit and Reality*, incidentally, is the title of a book by a blood brother whom I have discovered only recently.) For a long time reality for me was Woman. Which is equivalent to saying—Nature, Myth, Country, Mother, Chaos. I expatiate—to the reader's amazement, no doubt—on a romance called *She*, forgetting that I dedicated the cornerstone of my autobiography to "Her." How very much there was of "She" in "Her!" In place of the great Caves of Kôr I described the bottomless black pit. Like "She," "Her" also strove desperately to give me life, beauty, power and dominion over others, even if only through the magic of words. "Her's" too was an endless immolation, a waiting (in how awful a sense!) for the Beloved to return. And if "Her" dealt me death in the Place of Life, was it not also in blind passion, out of fear and jealousy? What was the secret of Her terrible beauty, Her fearful power over others, Her contempt for Her slavish minions, if not the desire to expiate Her crime? *The crime?* That she had robbed me of my identity at the very moment when I was about to recover it. In Her I lived as truly as the image of the slain Kallikrates lived in the mind, heart and soul of Ayesha. In some strange, twisted way, having dedicated myself to the task of immortalizing Her, I convinced myself that I was giving Her Life in return for Death. I thought I could resurrect the past, thought I could make it live again—*in truth*. Vanity, vanity! All I accomplished was to reopen the wound that had been inflicted upon me. The wound still lives, and with the pain of it comes the remembrance of what I was. I see very clearly that I was not this, not that. The "notness" is clearer than the "isness." I see the meaning of the long Odyssey I made; I recognize *all* the Circes who held me in their thrall. I found my father, both the one in the flesh and the unnameable one. And I discovered that father and son are one. More, immeasurably more: I found at last that all is one.

At Mycenae, standing before the grave of Clytemnestra, I relived the ancient Greek tragedies which nourished me more than did the great Shakespeare. Climbing down the slippery stairs to the pit, which I described in the book on Greece, I experienced the same sensation of horror which I did as a boy when descending into the bowels of Kôr. It seems to me that I have stood before many a bottomless pit, have looked into many a charnel house, but what is more vivid still, more awe-inspiring, is the remembrance that, whenever in my life I have gazed too long upon Beauty, particularly the beauty of the female, I have always experienced the sensation of fear. Fear, and a touch of horror too. What is the origin of this horror? The dim remembrance of being other than I now am, of being fit (once) to receive the blessings of beauty, the gift of love, the truth of God. Why, do we not sometimes ask ourselves, why the fatidical beauty in the great heroines of love throughout the ages? Why do they seem so logically and naturally surrounded by death, bolstered by crime, nourished by evil? There is a sentence in *She* which is strikingly penetrative. It comes at the moment when Ayesha, having found her Beloved, realizes that physical union must be postponed yet a while. "As yet I may not mate with thee, for thou and I are different, and the very brightness of my being would burn thee up, and perchance destroy thee." (I would give anything to know what I made of these words when I read them as a boy!)

No matter how much I dwell on the works of others I come back inevitably to the one and only book, the book of myself.

"Can I be," says Miguel de Unamuno, "as I believe myself or as others believe me to be? Here is where these lines become a confession in the presence of my unknown and unknowable me, unknown and unknowable for myself. Here is where I create the legend wherein I must bury myself."

These lines appear in the fly-leaf to *Black Spring,* a book which came nearer to being myself, I believe, than any book I have written before or since. The book which I had promised myself to create as a monument to Her, the book in which I was to deliver the "secret," I did not have the courage to begin until about eight years ago. And then, having begun it, I put it aside for another five years. *Tropic of Capricorn* was intended to be the cornerstone of this monumental work. It is more like a vestibule or ante-chamber. The truth is that I wrote this dread book* in my head when jotting down (in the space of about eighteen continuous hours) the complete outline or notes covering the subject matter of this work. I made this cryptic skeleton of the magnum opus during a period of brief separation—from "Her." I was completely possessed and utterly desolate. It is now almost twenty-three years to the dot that I laid out the plan of the book. I had no thought whatever then of writing anything but this one grand book. It was to be the Book of My Life—my life with Her. Of what stupendous, unimaginable detours are our lives composed! All is voyage, all is quest. We are not even aware of the goal until we have reached it and become one with it. To employ the word reality is to say myth and legend. To speak of creation means to bury oneself in chaos. We know not whence we come nor whither we go, nor even who we are. We set sail for the golden shores, sped on sometimes like "arrows of longing," and we arrive at our destination in the full glory of realization—or else as unrecognizable pulp from which the essence of life has been squashed. But let us not be deceived by the word "failure" which attaches itself to certain illustrious names and which is nothing more than the written seal and symbol of martyrdom. When the good Dr. Gachet wrote to brother Theo that the expression "love of art" did not apply in Vincent's case, that his was rather a case of "martyrdom" to his art, we realize with full hearts that Van Gogh was one of the most glorious "failures" in the history of art. Similarly, when Professor

* *The Rosy Crucifixion.*

Dandieu states that Proust was "the most living of the dead," we understand immediately that this "living corpse" had walled himself in to expose the absurdity and the emptiness of our feverish activity. Montaigne from his "retreat" throws a beam of light down the centuries. *The Failure,* by Papini, incited me enormously and helped to erase from my mind all thought of failure. If Life and Death are very near together, so are success and failure.

It is our great fortune sometimes to misinterpret our destiny when it is revealed to us. We often accomplish our ends despite ourselves. We try to avoid the swamps and jungles, we seek frantically to escape the wilderness or the desert (one and the same), we attach ourselves to leaders, we worship the gods instead of the One and Only, we lose ourselves in the labyrinth, we fly to distant shores and speak with other tongues, adopt other customs, manners, conventions, but ever and always are we driven towards our true end, concealed from us till the last moment.

■ ■

OBSCENITY AND THE
LAW OF REFLECTION

To DISCUSS the nature and meaning of obscenity is almost as difficult as to talk about God. Until I began delving into the literature which has grown up about the subject I never realized what a morass I was wading into. If one begins with etymology one is immediately aware that lexicographers are bamboozlers every bit as much as jurists, moralists and politicians. To begin with, those who have seriously attempted to track down the meaning of the term are obliged to confess that they have arrived nowhere. In their book, *To the Pure,* Ernst and Seagle state that "no two persons agree on the definitions of the six deadly adjectives: obscene, lewd, lascivious, filthy, indecent, disgusting." The League of Nations was also stumped when it attempted to define what constituted obscenity. D. H. Lawrence was probably right when he said that "nobody knows what the word obscene means." As for Theodore Schroeder, who has devoted his whole life to fighting for freedom of speech,* his opinion is that "obscenity does not exist in any book or picture, but is wholly a quality of the reading or viewing mind." "No argument for the suppression of obscene literature," he states, "has ever been offered which by unavoidable implications will not justify, and which has not already justified, every other limitation that has ever been put upon mental freedom."

As someone has well said, to name all the masterpieces

* See his *A Challenge to Sex Censors* and other works.

which have been labeled obscene would make a tedious catalogue. Most of our choice writers, from Plato to Have-lock Ellis, from Aristophanes to Shaw, from Catullus and Ovid to Shakespeare, Shelley and Swinburne, together with the Bible, to be sure, have been the target of those who are forever in search of what is impure, indecent and immoral. In an article called *"Freedom of Expression in Litera-ture,"** Huntington Cairns, one of the most broadminded and clear-sighted of all the censors, stresses the need for the re-education of officials charged with law enforcement. "In general," he states, "such men have had little or no contact with science or art, have had no knowledge of the liberty of expression tacitly granted to men of letters since the beginnings of English literature, and have been, from the point of view of expert opinion, altogether incompetent to handle the subject. Administrative officials, not the populace who in the main have only a negligible contact with art, stand first in need of re-education."

Perhaps it should be noted here, in passing, that though our Federal government exercises no censorship over works of art originating in the country, it does permit the Treasury Department to pass judgments upon importations from abroad. In 1930, the Tariff Act was revised to permit the Secretary of the Treasury, in his discretion, to admit the classics or books of recognized and established literary or scientific merit, even if obscene. What is meant by "books of recognized and established literary merit?" Mr. Cairns gives us the following interpretation: "books which have behind them a substantial and reputable body of American critical opinion indicating that the works are of meritorious quality." This would seem to represent a fairly liberal attitude, but when it comes to a test, when a book or other work of art is capable of creating a furore, this seem-ing liberality collapses. It has been said with regard to the Sonnets of Aretino that they were condemned for four hundred years. How long we shall have to wait for the ban to be lifted on certain famous contemporary works no one can predict. In the article alluded to above, Mr. Cairns admits that "there is no likelihood whatever that the present

* From the *Annals of the American Academy of Political and Social Science,* Philadelphia, November, 1938.

obscenity statutes will be repealed." "None of the statutes," he goes on to say, "defines the word 'obscenity' and there is thus a wide latitude of discretion in the meaning to be attributed to the term." Those who imagine that the *Ulysses* decision established a precedent should realize by now that they were over-optimistic. Nothing has been established where books of a disturbing nature are concerned. After years of wrestling with prudes, bigots and other psychopaths who determine what we may or may not read, Theodore Schroeder is of the opinion that "it is not the inherent quality of the book which counts, but its hypothetical influence upon some hypothetical person, who at some problematical time in the future may hypothetically read the book."

In his book called *A Challenge to the Sex Censors,* Mr. Schroeder quotes an anonymous clergyman of a century ago to the effect that "obscenity exists only in the minds that discover it and charge others with it." This obscure work contains most illuminating passages; in it the author attempts to show that, by a law of reflection in nature, everyone is the performer of acts similar to those he attributes to others; that self-preservation is self-destruction, etc. This wholesome and enlightened viewpoint, attainable, it would seem, only by the rare few, comes nearer to dissipating the fogs which envelop the subject than all the learned treatises of educators, moralists, scholars and jurists combined. In Romans XIV: 14 we have it presented to us axiomatically for all time: "I know and am persuaded by the Lord Jesus that there is nothing unclean of itself, but to him that esteemeth anything to be unclean, to him it is unclean." How far one would get in the courts with this attitude, or what the postal authorities would make of it, surely no sane individual has any doubts about.

A totally different point of view, and one which deserves attention, since it is not only honest and forthright but expressive of the innate conviction of many, is that voiced by Havelock Ellis, that obscenity is a "permanent element of human social life and corresponds to a deep need of the human mind." * Ellis indeed goes so far as to say that "adults need obscene literature, as much as children need

* *More Essays of Love and Virtue.*

fairy tales, as a relief from the oppressive force of convention." This is the attitude of a cultured individual whose
purity and wisdom has been acknowledged by eminent
critics everywhere. It is the worldly view which we profess
to admire in the Mediterranean peoples. Ellis, being an
Englishman, was of course persecuted for his opinions and
ideas upon the subject of sex. From the nineteenth century
on all English authors who dared to treat the subject honestly and realistically have been persecuted and humiliated.
The prevalent attitude of the English people is, I believe,
fairly well presented in such a piece of polished inanity as
Viscount Brentford's righteous self-defense—*"Do We
Need a Censor?"* Viscount Brentford is the gentleman who
tried to protect the English public from such iniquitous
works as *Ulysses* and *The Well of Loneliness*. He is the
type, so rampant in the Anglo-Saxon world, to which the
words of Dr. Ernest Jones would seem to apply: "It is
the people with secret attractions to various temptations
who busy themselves with removing these temptations from
other people; really they are defending themselves under
the pretext of defending others, because at heart they fear
their own weakness."

As one accused of employing obscene language more
freely and abundantly than any other living writer in the
English language, it may be of interest to present my own
views on the subject. Since the *Tropic of Cancer* first appeared in Paris, in 1934, I have received many hundreds
of letters from readers all over the world; they are from
men and women of all ages and all walks of life, and in the
main they are congratulatory messages. Many of those
who denounced the book because of its gutter language
professed admiration for it otherwise; very, very few ever
remarked that it was a dull book, or badly written. The
book continues to sell steadily "under the counter" and is
still written about at intervals although it made its appearance thirteen years ago and was promptly banned in all the
Anglo-Saxon countries. The only effect which censorship
has had upon its circulation is to drive it underground, thus
limiting the sales but at the same time insuring for it the
best of all publicity—word of mouth recommendation. It
is to be found in the libraries of nearly all our important

colleges, is often recommended to students by their professors, and has gradually come to take its place beside other celebrated literary works which, once similarly banned and suppressed, are now accepted as classics. It is a book which appeals especially to young people and which, from all that I gather directly and indirectly, not only does not ruin their lives, but increases their morale. The book is a living proof that censorship defeats itself. It also proves once again that the only ones who may be said to be protected by censorship are the censors themselves, and this only because of a law of nature known to all who over-indulge. In this connection I feel impelled to mention a curious fact often brought to my attention by booksellers, namely that the two classes of books which enjoy a steady and ever-increasing sale are the so-called pornographic, or obscene, and the occult. This would seem to corroborate Havelock Ellis's view which I mentioned earlier. Certainly all attempts to regulate the traffic in obscene books, just as all attempts to regulate the traffic in drugs or prostitution, is doomed to failure wherever civilization rears its head. Whether these things are a definite evil or not, whether or not they are definite and ineradicable elements of our social life, it seems indisputable that they are synonymous with what is called civilization. Despite all that has been said and written for and against, it is evident that with regard to these factors of social life men have never come to that agreement which they have about slavery. It is possible, of course, that one day these things may disappear, but it is also possible, despite the now seemingly universal disapproval of it, that slavery may once again be practiced by human beings.

The most insistent question put to the writer of "obscene" literature is: why did you have to use such language? The implication is, of course, that with conventional terms or means the same effect might have been obtained. Nothing, of course, could be further from the truth. Whatever the language employed, no matter how objectionable —I am here thinking of the most extreme examples—one may be certain that there was no other idiom possible. Effects are bound up with intentions, and these in turn are governed by laws of compulsion as rigid as nature's own. That is something which non-creative individuals seldom ever understand. Someone has said that "the literary artist, having attained understanding, communicates that understanding to his readers. That understanding, whether of sexual or other matters, is certain to come into conflict with popular beliefs, fears and taboos, because these are, for the most part, based on error." Whatever extenuating reasons are adduced for the erroneous opinions of the populace, such as lack of education, lack of contact with the arts, and so on, the fact is that there will always be a gulf between the creative artist and the public because the latter is immune to the mystery inherent in and surrounding all creation. The struggle which the artist wages, consciously or unconsciously, with the public, centers almost exclusively about the problem of a necessitous choice. Putting to one side all questions of ego and temperament, and taking the broadest view of the creative process, which makes of the artist nothing more than an instrument, we are nevertheless forced to conclude that the spirit of an age is the crucible in which, through one means or another, certain vital and mysterious forces seek expression. If there is something mysterious about the manifestation of deep and unsuspected forces, which find expression in disturbing movements and ideas from one period to another, there is nevertheless nothing accidental or bizarre about it. The laws governing the spirit are just as readable as those governing nature. But the readings must come from those who are steeped in the mysteries. The very depth of these interpretations naturally make them unpalatable and unacceptable to the vast body which constitutes the unthinking public.

Parenthetically it is curious to observe that painters, however unapproachable their work may be, are seldom subjected to the same meddling interference as writers. Language, because it also serves as a means of communication, tends to bring about weird obfuscations. Men of high intelligence often display execrable taste when it comes to the arts. Yet even these freaks whom we all recognize, because we are always amazed by their obtuseness, seldom have the cheek to say what elements of a picture had been better left out or what substitutions might have been effected. Take, for example, the early works of George

Grosz. Compare the reactions of the intelligent public in his case to the reactions provoked by Joyce when his *Ulysses* appeared. Compare these again with the reactions which Schoenberg's later music inspired. In the case of all three the revulsion which their work first induced was equally strong, but in the case of Joyce the public was more articulate, more voluble, more arrogant in its pseudo-certitude. With books even the butcher and the plumber seem to feel that they have a right to an opinion, especially if the book happens to be what is called a filthy or disgusting one.

I have noticed, moreover, that the attitude of the public alters perceptibly when it is the work of primitive peoples which they must grapple with. Here for some obscure reason the element of the "obscene" is treated with more deference. People who would be revolted by the drawings in *Ecce Homo* will gaze unblushingly at African pottery or sculpture no matter how much their taste or morals may be offended. In the same spirit they are inclined to be more tolerant of the obscene works of ancient authors. Why? Because even the dullest are capable of admitting to themselves that other epochs might, justifiably or not, have enjoyed other customs, other morals. As for the creative spirits of their own epoch, however, freedom of expression is always interpreted as license. The artist must conform to the current and usually hypocritical, attitude of the majority. He must be original, courageous, inspiring and all that—but never too disturbing. He must say Yes while saying No. The larger the art public, the more tyrannical, complex and perverse does this irrational pressure become. There are always exceptions, to be sure, and Picasso is one of them, one of the few artists in our time table to command the respect and attention of a bewildered and largely hostile public. It is the greatest tribute that could be made to his genius.

The chances are that during this transition period of global wars, lasting perhaps a century or two, art will become less and less important. A world torn by indescribable upheavals, a world preoccupied with social and political transformations, will have less time and energy to spare for the creation and appreciation of works of art. The politician, the soldier, the industrialist, the technician, all those in short who cater to immediate needs, to creature comforts, to transitory and illusory passions and prejudices, will take precedence over the artist. The most poetic inventions will be those capable of serving the most destructive ends. Poetry itself will be expressed in terms of block-busters and lethal gases. The obscene will find expression in the most unthinkable techniques of self-destruction which the inventive genius of man will be forced to adopt. The revolt and disgust which the prophetic spirits in the realm of art have inspired, through their vision of a world in the making, will find justification in the years to come as these dreams are acted out.

The growing void between art and life, art becoming ever more sensational and unintelligible, life becoming more dull and hopeless, has been commented on almost ad nauseum. The war, colossal and portentous as it is, has failed to arouse a passion commensurate with its scope or significance. The fervor of the Greeks and the Spaniards was something which astounded the modern world. The admiration and the horror which their ferocious struggles evoked was revelatory. We regarded them as mad and heroic, and we had almost been on the point of believing that such madness, such heroism, no longer existed. But what strikes one as "obscene" and insane rather than mad is the stupendous machine-like character of the war which the big nations are carrying on. It is a war of materiel, a war of statistical preponderance, a war in which victory is coldly and patiently calculated on the basis of bigger and better resources. In the war which the Spaniards and the Greeks waged there was not only a hopelessness about the immediate outcome but a hopelessness as to the eternal outcome, so to speak. Yet they fought, and with tooth and nail, and they will fight again and again, always hopelessly and always gloriously because always passionately. As for the big powers now locked in a death struggle, one feels that they are only grooming themselves for another chance at it, for a chance to win here and now in a victory that will be everlasting, which is an utter delusion. Whatever the outcome, one senses that life will not be altered radically but to a degree which will only make it more like what it was before the conflict started. This war has all the masturbative qualities of a combat between hopeless recidivists.

If I stress the obscene aspect of modern warfare it is not simply because I am against war but because there is something about the ambivalent emotions it inspires which enables me better to grapple with the nature of the obscene. Nothing would be regarded as obscene, I feel, if men were living out their inmost desires. What man dreads most is to be faced with the manifestation, in word or deed, of that which he has refused to live out, that which he has throttled or stifled, buried, as we say now, in his subconscious mind. The sordid qualities imputed to the enemy are always those which we recognize as our own and therefore rise to slay, because only through projection do we realize the enormity and horror of them. Man tries as in a dream to kill the enemy in himself. This enemy, both within and without, is just as, but no more, real than the phantoms in his dreams. When awake he is apathetic about this dream self, but asleep he is filled with terror. I say "when awake," but the question is, *when is he awake, if ever?* To those who no longer need to kill, the man who indulges in murder is a sleep walker. He is a man trying to kill himself in his dreams. He is a man who comes face to face with himself *only in the dream.* This man is the man of the modern world, everyman, as much a myth and a legend as the Everyman of the allegory. Our life to-day is what we dreamed it would be aeons ago. Always it has a double thread running through it, just as in the age-old dream. Always fear and wish, fear and wish. Never the pure fountain of desire. And so we have and we have not, we are and we are not.

In the realm of sex there is a similar kind of sleepwalking and self-delusion at work; here the bifurcation of pure desire into fear and wish has resulted in the creation of a phantasmagorical world in which love plays the role of a chameleon-like scapegoat. Passion is conspicuous by its absence or by monstrous deformations which render it practically unrecognizable. To trace the history of man's attitude towards sex is like threading a labyrinth whose heart is situated in an unknown planet. There has been so much distortion and suppression, even among primitive peoples, that to-day it is virtually impossible to say what constitutes a free and healthy attitude. Certainly the glorification of sex, in pagan times, represented no solution of the problem. And, though Christianity ushered in a conception of love superior to any known before, it did not succeed in freeing man sexually. Perhaps we might say that the tyranny of sex was broken through sublimation in love, but the nature of this greater love has been understood and experienced only by a rare few.

Only where strict bodily discipline is observed, for the purpose of union or communion with God, has the subject of sex ever been faced squarely. Those who have achieved emancipation by this route have, of course, not only liberated themselves from the tyranny of sex but from all other tyrannies of the flesh. With such individuals, the whole body of desire has become so transfigured that the results obtained have had practically no meaning for the man of the world. Spiritual triumphs, even though they affect the man in the street immediately, concern him little, if at all. He is seeking for a solution of life's problems on the plane of mirage and delusion; his notions of reality have nothing to do with ultimate effects; he is blind to the permanent changes which take place above and beneath his level of understanding. If we take such a type of being as the Yogi, whose sole concern is with reality, as opposed to the world of illusion, we are bound to concede that he has faced every human problem with the utmost courage and lucidity. Whether he incorporates the sexual or transmutes it to the point of transcendence and obliteration, he is at least one who has attained to the vast open spaces of love. If he does not reproduce his kind, he at least gives new meaning to the word birth. In lieu of copulating he creates; in the circle of his influence conflict is stilled and the harmony of a profound peace established. He is able to love not only individuals of the opposite sex but all individuals, everything that breathes, in fact. This quiet sort of triumph strikes a chill in the heart of the ordinary man, for not only does it make him visualize the loss of his meagre sex life but the loss of passion itself, passion as he knows it. This sort of liberation, which smashes his thermometrical gauge of feeling, represents itself to him as a living death. The attainment of a love which is boundless and unfettered terrifies him for the very good reason that it means the dissolution of his ego. He does not want to be freed for service, dedication and devotion to all mankind; he wants comfort, assurance and security, the enjoyment of his very limited powers. Incapable of surrender, he can never know the healing power of faith; and lacking faith he can never begin to know the meaning of love. He seeks release but not liberation, which is like saying that he prefers death instead of life.

As civilization progresses it becomes more and more apparent that war is the greatest release which life offers the ordinary man. Here he can let go to his heart's content for here crime no longer has any meaning. Guilt is abolished when the whole planet swims in blood. The lulls of peacetime seem only to permit him to sink deeper into the bogs of the sadistic-masochistic complex which has fastened itself into the heart of our civilized life like a cancer. Fear, guilt and murder—these constitute the real triumvirate which rules our lives. *What is obscene then?* The whole fabric of life as we know it to-day. To speak only of what is indecent, foul, lewd, filthy, disgusting, etc., in connection with sex, is to deny ourselves the luxury of the great gamut of revulsion-repulsion which modern life puts at our service. Every department of life is vitiated and corroded with what is so unthinkingly labeled "obscene." One wonders if perhaps the insane could not invent a more fitting, more inclusive term for the polluting elements of life which we create and shun and never identify with our behavior. We think of the insane as inhabiting a world completely divorced from reality, but our own everyday behavior, whether in war or peace, if examined from only a slightly higher standpoint, bears all the earmarks of insanity. "I have said," writes a well-known psychologist, "that this is a mad world, that man is most of the time mad; and I believe that in a way what we call morality is merely a form of madness, which happens to be a working adaptation to existing circumstances."

When obscenity crops out in art, in literature more particularly, it usually functions as a technical device; the element of the deliberate which is there has nothing to do with sexual excitation, as in pornography. If there is an ulterior motive at work it is one which goes far beyond sex. Its purpose is to awaken, to usher in a sense of reality. In a sense, its use by the artist may be compared to the use of the miraculous by the Masters. This last minute quality, so closely allied to desperation, has been the subject of endless debate. Nothing connected with Christ's life, for example, has been exposed to such withering scrutiny as the miracles attributed to him. The great question is: should the Master indulge himself or should he refrain from employing his extraordinary powers? Of the great Zen masters it has been observed that they never hesitate to resort to any means in order to awaken their disciples; they will even perform what we would call sacrilegious acts. And, according to some familiar interpretations of the Flood, it has been acknowledged that even God grows desperate at times and wipes the slate clean in order to continue the human experiment on another level.

It should be recognized, however, with regard to these questionable displays of power, that only a Master may hazard them. As a matter of fact, the element of risk exists only in the eyes of the uninitiated. The Master is always certain of the result; he never plays his trump card, as it were, except at the psychological moment. His behavior, in such instances, might be compared to that of the chemist pouring a last tiny drop into a prepared solution in order to precipitate certain salts. If it is a push it is also a supreme exhortation which the Master indulges in. Once the moment is passed, moreover, the witness is altered forever. In another sense, the situation might be described as the transition from belief to faith. Once faith has been established, there is no regression; whereas with belief everything is in suspense and capable of fluctuation.

It should also be recognized that those who have real power have no need to demonstrate it for themselves; it is never in their own interests, or for their own glorification, that these performances are made. In fact, there is nothing miraculous, in the vulgar sense, about these acts, unless it be the ability to raise the consciousness of the onlooker to that mysterious level of illumination which is natural to the Master. Men who are ignorant of the source of their powers, on the other hand, men who are regarded as the powers that move the world, usually come to a disastrous end. Of their efforts it is truly said that all comes to nought. On the worldly level nothing endures, because on this level, which is the level of dream and delusion, all is fear and wish vainly cemented by will.

To revert to the artist again . . . Once he has made use of his extraordinary powers, and I am thinking of the use of obscenity in just such magical terms, he is inevitably caught up in the stream of forces beyond him. He may have begun by assuming that he could awaken his readers, but in the end he himself passes into another dimension of reality wherein he no longer feels the need of forcing an awakening. His rebellion over the prevalent inertia about him becomes transmuted, as his vision increases, into an acceptance and understanding of an order and harmony which is beyond man's conception and approachable only through faith. His vision expands with the growth of his own powers, because creation has its roots in vision and admits of only one realm, the realm of imagination. Ultimately, then, he stands among his own obscene objurgations like the conqueror midst the ruins of a devastated city. He realizes that the real nature of the obscene resides in the lust to convert. He knocked to awaken, but it was himself he awakened. And once awake, he is no longer concerned with the world of sleep; he walks in the light and, like a mirror, reflects his illumination in every act.

Once this vantage point is reached, how trifling and remote seem the accusations of moralists! How senseless the debate as to whether the work in question was of high literary merit or not! How absurd the wrangling over the moral or immoral nature of his creation! Concerning every bold act one may raise the reproach of vulgarity. Everything dramatic is in the nature of an appeal, a frantic appeal for communion. Violence, whether in deed or speech, is an inverted sort of prayer. Initiation itself is a violent process of purification and union. Whatever demands radical treatment demands God, and always through some form of death or annihilation. Whenever the obscene crops out one can smell the imminent death of a form. Those who possess the highest clue are not impatient, even in the presence of death; the artist in words, however, is not of this order, he is only at the vestibule, as it were, of the palace of wisdom. Dealing with the spirit, he nevertheless has recourse to forms. When he fully understands his role as creator he substitutes his own being for the medium of words. But in that process there comes the "dark night of the soul" when, exalted by his vision of things to come and not yet fully conscious of his powers, he resorts to violence. He becomes desperate over his inability to transmit his vision. He resorts to any and every means in his power; this agony, in which creation itself is parodied, prepares him for the solution of his dilemma, but a solution wholly unforeseen and mysterious as creation itself.

All violent manifestations of radiant power have an obscene glow when visualized through the refractive lens of the ego. All conversions occur in the speed of a split second. Liberation implies the sloughing off of chains, the bursting of the cocoon. What is obscene are the preliminary or anticipatory movements of birth, the preconscious writhing in the face of a life to be. It is in the agony of death that the nature of birth is apprehended. For in what consists the struggle if it is not between form and being, between that which was and that which is about to be? In such moments creation itself is at the bar; whoever seeks to unveil the mystery becomes himself a part of the mystery and thus helps to perpetuate it. Thus the lifting of the veil may be interpreted as the ultimate expression of the obscene. It is an attempt to spy on the secret processes of the universe. In this sense the guilt attaching to Prometheus symbolizes the guilt of man-the-creator, of man-the-arrogant-one who ventures to create before being crowned with wisdom.

The pangs of birth relate not to the body but to the spirit. It was demanded of us to know love, experience union and communion, and thus achieve liberation from the wheel of life and death. But we have chosen to remain this side of Paradise and to create through art the illusory substance of our dreams. In a profound sense we are forever delaying the act. We flirt with destiny and lull ourselves to sleep with myth. We die in the throes of our own tragic legends, like spiders caught in their own webs. If there is anything which deserves to be called "obscene" it is this oblique, glancing confrontation with the mysteries, this walking up to the edge of the abyss, enjoying all the ecstasies of vertigo and yet refusing to yield to the spell of the unknown. The obscene has all the qualities of the hidden interval. It is as vast as the Unconscious itself and as amorphous and fluid as the very stuff of the Unconscious. It is what comes to the surface as strange, intoxicating and forbidden, and which therefore arrests and paralyzes, when in the form of Narcissus we bend over our own image in the mirror of our own iniquity. Acknowledged by all, it is nevertheless despised and rejected, wherefore it is constantly emerging in Protean guise at the most unexpected moments. When it is recognized and accepted, whether as a figment of the imagination or as an integral part of human reality, it inspires no more dread or revulsion than could be ascribed to the flowering lotus which sends its roots down into the mud of the stream on which it is borne.

REUNION IN BROOKLYN

I ARRIVED AT THE DOCK in practically the same condition in which I had left, that is, penniless. I had been away exactly ten years. It seemed much longer, more like twenty or thirty. What sustained me more than anything else during my residence abroad was the belief that I would never be obliged to return to America.

I had of course kept up a correspondence with the family during this period; it was not a very fulsome correspondence and I am sure it gave them very little idea of what my life really was like. Towards the end of my stay in Paris I received a letter informing me of my father's illness; the nature of it was such that I entertained little hope of finding him alive on my return.

What plagued me all the time I was away, and with renewed force as I was crossing the ocean, was the realization that I could give them no help. In the fifteen years which had elapsed since I began my career I had not only proved incapable of supporting myself by my efforts but I had substantially increased my debts. I was not only penniless, as when I left, but I was further in the hole, so that actually my position was far worse than on leaving the country. All I had to my credit were a few books which more than likely will never be published in this country, at least not as they were written. The few gifts which I had brought with me I was obliged to leave at the Customs because I lacked the money to pay the necessary duty.

As we were going through the immigration formalities

the officer asked me jokingly if I were *the* Henry Miller to which I replied in the same vein that the one he meant was dead. He knew that, of course. Asked as to what I had been doing in Europe all that time I said—"enjoying myself"—an answer which had the double merit of being true and of forestalling further questions.

Almost the first words out of my mother's mouth, after we had greeted each other, were: "Can't you write something like *Gone With the Wind* and make a little money?" I had to confess I couldn't. I seem to be congenitally incapable of writing a best seller. At Boston, where we first put in, I remember my astonishment on wandering through the railway station when I saw the staggering heaps of books and magazines for sale. (It was my first glimpse of America and I was rather dazzled and bewildered.) *Gone With the Wind* was all over the place, apparently, in a cheap movie edition which looked more interesting to me, accustomed to the paper-covered books of France, than the original format. I wondered vaguely how many millions of dollars had been put in circulation by this book. I noticed that there were other women writers whose works were displayed among the bestsellers. They all seemed to be huge tomes capable of satisfying the most voracious reader. It seemed perfectly natural to me that the women writers of America should occupy such a prominent place. America is essentially a woman's country—why shouldn't the leading novelists be women?

How I had dreaded this moment of returning to the bosom of the family! The thought of walking down this street again had always been a nightmare to me. If any one had told me when in Greece that two months hence I would be doing this I would have told him he was crazy. And yet, when I was informed at the American Consulate in Athens that I would be obliged to return to America I made no effort to resist. I accepted their unwarranted interference as if I were obeying the voice of Fate. Deep down, I suppose, was the realization that I had left something unfinished in America. Moreover, when the summons came I must confess that I was morally and spiritually stronger than I had ever been in my life. "If need be," I said to myself, "I can go back to America," much as one would say, "I feel strong enough to face anything now!"

Nevertheless, once back in New York it took me several weeks to prepare myself for the ordeal. I had, of course, written my folks that I was on my way. They very naturally expected me to telephone them immediately on my arrival. It was cruel not to do so but I was so intent on easing my own pain that I postponed communicating with them for a week or more. Finally I wrote them from Virginia, where I had fled almost at once, unable to bear the sight of my native city. What I was hoping for above all, in trying to gain a little time, was a sudden turn of fortune, the advent of a few hundred dollars from a publisher or editor, some little sum with which to save my face. Well, nothing turned up. The one person whom I had vaguely counted on failed me. I mean my American publisher. He hadn't even been willing to assist me in getting back to America, so I learned. He feared that if he sent me the passage money I would squander it on drink or in some other foolish way. He probably means well and he certainly writes well about honoring the artist in our midst, giving him food and drink and that sort of thing. *"Welcome home, Henry Miller. . . ."* I often thought of that phrase of his which he inserted in the preface of my book as I turned about in the rat trap. It's easy to write such things, but to substantiate words with deeds is quite another matter.

It was towards evening when I set out to visit the folks. I came up out of the new Eighth Avenue subway and, though I knew the neighborhood well, immediately proceeded to lose my bearings. Not that the neighborhood had changed much; if anything it was I who had changed. I had changed so completely that I couldn't find my way any more in the old surroundings. I suppose too that getting lost was a last unconscious effort to avoid the ordeal.

As I came down the block where the house stands it seemed to me as if nothing had changed. I was infuriated, in fact, to think that this street which I loathe so much had been so impervious to the march of time. I forget. . . . There was *one* important change. On the corner where the German grocery store had been, and where I had been horsewhipped as a boy, there now stood a funeral parlor.

A rather significant transformation! But what was even more striking is the fact that the undertaker had originally been a neighbor of ours—in the old 14th Ward which we had left years ago. I recognized the name at once. It gave me a creepy feeling, passing his place. Had he divined that we would shortly be in need of his services?

As I approached the gate I saw my father sitting in the armchair by the window. The sight of him sitting there, waiting for me, gave me a terrible pang. It was as though he had been sitting there waiting all these years. I felt at once like a criminal, like a murderer.

It was my sister who opened the iron gate. She had altered considerably, had shrunk and withered like a Chinese nut. My mother and father were standing at the threshold to greet me. They had aged terribly. For the space of a moment I had the uncomfortable sensation of gazing at two mummies who had been removed from the vault and galvanized into a semblance of life. We embraced one another and then we stood apart in silence for another fleeting moment during which I comprehended in a flash the appalling tragedy of their life and of my own life and of every animate creature's on earth. In that moment all the strength which I had accumulated to fortify myself was undone; I was emptied of everything but an overwhelming compassion. When suddenly my mother said, "Well, Henry, how do we look to you?" I let out a groan followed by the most heart-rending sobs. I wept as I had never wept before. My father, to conceal his own feelings, withdrew to the kitchen. I hadn't removed my coat and my hat was still in my hand. In the blinding flood of tears everything was swimming before my eyes. "God Almighty!" I thought to myself, "what have I done? Nothing I thought to accomplish justifies this. I should have remained, I should have sacrificed myself for them. Perhaps there is still time. Perhaps I can do so *something* to prove that I am not utterly selfish. . . ." My mother meanwhile said nothing. Nobody uttered a word. I stood there in the middle of the room with my overcoat on and my hat in my hand and I wept until there were no more tears left. When I had collected myself a bit I dried my eyes and looked about the room. It was the same immaculate place, showing not the least sign of wear or tear, glowing a little brighter, if anything, than before. Or did I imagine it because of my guilt? At any rate, I thanked God, it did not seem poverty-stricken as I had feared it might look. It was the same modest, humble place it had always been. It was like a polished mausoleum in which their misery and suffering had been kept brightly burning.

The table was set; we were to eat in a few moments. It seemed natural that it should be thus, though I hadn't the slightest desire to eat. In the past the great emotional scenes which I had witnessed in the bosom of the family were nearly always associated with the table. We pass easily from sorrow to gluttony.

We sat down in our accustomed places, looking somewhat more cheerful, if not actually merry, than we had a few moments ago. The storm had passed; there would only be slight and distant reverberations henceforth. I had hardly taken the spoon in my hand when they all began to talk at once. They had been waiting for this moment a long time; they wanted to pour out in a few minutes all that had been accumulating for ten years. Never have I felt so willing to listen. Had they poured it out for twenty-four hours on end I would have sat patiently, without a murmur, without a sign of restlessness, until the last word had been uttered. Now at last they had me and could tell me everything. They were so eager to begin, so beside themselves with joy, that it all came out in a babble. It was almost as if they feared that I would run off again and stay away another ten years.

It was about time for the war news and so they turned the radio on, thinking that I would be interested. In the midst of the babble and confusion, boats going down, ammunition works blasted, and the same smooth dentifricial voice switching from calamities to razor blades without a change of intonation or inflection, my mother interrupted the hubbub to tell me that they had been thinking about my homecoming and had planned that I should share a bed with my father. She said she would sleep with my sister in the little room where I had slept as a boy. That brought on another choking fit. I told them there was no need to worry about such things, that I had already found a place to stay and that everything was jake. I tried to tell them jokingly that I was now a celebrity, but it didn't sound very convincing either to them or to myself.

"Of course," said my mother, ignoring what I had just said, "it may be a little inconvenient for you, father has to get up now and then during the night—but you'll get used to it. I don't hear him any more."

I looked at my father. "Yes," he said, "since the operation, the last one, I'm lucky if I get three or four hours' sleep." He drew aside his chair and pulled up the leg of his trousers to show me the bag which was strapped to his leg. "That's what I have to wear now," he said. "I can't urinate any more the natural way. It's a nuisance, but what can you do? They did the best they could for me." And he went on hurriedly to tell me of how good the doctor had been to him, though he was a perfect stranger and a Jew to boot. "Yes," he added, "they took me to the Jewish hospital. And I must say I couldn't have had better treatment anywhere."

I wondered how that had come about—the Jewish hospital—because my mother had always been scared to death of anything remotely connected with the Jews. The explanation was quite simple. They had outlived the family doctor and all the other doctors in the neighborhood whom they once knew. At the last moment some one had recommended the Jewish doctor, and since he was not only a specialist but a surgeon they had acquiesced. To their astonishment he had proved to be not only a good doctor but an extremely kind and sympathetic person. "He treated me as if he were my own son," said my father. Even my mother had to admit that they couldn't have found a better man. What seemed to impress them most about the hospital, I was amazed to learn, was the wonderful grub which they served there. One could eat à la carte apparently—and as much as one cared to. But the nurses were not Jewish, they wanted me to know. They were Scandinavian for the most part. The Jews don't like such jobs, they explained. "You know, they never like to do the dirty work," said my mother.

In the midst of the narrative, hardly able to wait for my mother to finish, my father suddenly recalled that he had made a note of some questions he wished to put to me. He asked my sister to get the slip of paper for him. Whereupon, to my surprise, my sister calmly told him to wait, that she hadn't finished her meal yet. With that he gave me a look, as much as to say—"you see what I have to put up with here!" I got up and found the piece of paper on which he had listed the questions. My father put on his spectacles and began to read.

"Oh, first of all," he exclaimed, "what pier did you dock at?" I told him.

"That's what I thought," he said. *"Now,* what was the grub like on board the boat? Was it American cooking or Greek?"

The other questions were in a similar vein. Had we received the wireless news every day? Did I have to share my cabin with others? Did we sight any wrecks? And then this —which took me completely by surprise: *What is the Parthenon?*

I explained briefly what the Parthenon was.

"Well, that's all right," he said as though to say—"no need to go into that any further." "I only asked," he added, looking up over the top of his spectacles, "because mother said she thought it was a park. I knew it wasn't a park. How old did you say it was again?" He paused a moment to hmmm. "The place must be full of old relics," he added. Well, anyway, it must have been very interesting in Greece, that's what he thought. As for himself he had always wanted to see Italy—and London. He asked about Saville Row where the merchant tailors have their shops. "You say the tailors (meaning the workmen on the bench) are all English? No Jews or Italians, eh?" "No," I said, "they all seemed to be English, from their looks anyway." "That's queer," he reflected. "Must be a strange place, London."

He moved over to the arm-chair near the window. "I can't sit here very long," he said, "it sinks too low. In a moment I'll change to the hard chair. You see, with all this harness on it gets pretty uncomfortable at times, especially when it's warm." As he talked he kept pressing the long tube which ran down his leg. "You see, it's getting gritty again. Just like sand inside. You'd never think that you pass off all that solid matter in your urine, would you? It's the damnedest thing. I take all the medicines he prescribes religiously, but the damned stuff will accumulate. That's my condition, I suppose. When it gets too thick I have to go to the doctor and let him irrigate me. About once a month, that is. *And does that hurt!* Well, we won't talk about that now. Some times it's worse than other times. There was one time I thought I couldn't stand it any more—they must have heard me for blocks around. If everything goes well I can stretch the visits to five or six weeks. It's five dollars a crack, you know."

I ventured to suggest that it might be better if he went oftener instead of trying to stretch it out.

"That's just what I say," he responded promptly. "But mother says we have to economize—there's nothing coming in any more, you know. Of course she doesn't have to stand the pain."

I looked at my mother inquiringly. She was irritated that my father should have put it thus. "You can't run to the doctor every time you have a little pain," she said scoldingly, as if to rebuke him for having brought up the subject. "I've told him time and again that's his condition."

By condition she meant that he would have to endure his suffering until . . . well, if she had to put it baldly she would say—*until the end.* He was lucky to be alive, after all he had gone through. "If it weren't for that old bag, for that awful leakage," she ruminated aloud, "father would be all right. You see what an appetite he has—and what a color!"

"Yes," my sister put in, "he eats more than any of us. We do all the work; he has it easy."

My father gave me another look. My mother, catching his mute appeal, tried to pass it over lightly with a little joke, one of those crude jokes which the family were fond of. "Look at him," she said with a slightly hysterical laugh, "hasn't he a good color? Why, he's as tough as an old rooster. You couldn't kill him off with an axe!"

It was impossible for me to laugh at this. But my sister, who had learned to take her cue from my mother, suddenly grew apoplectic with indignation. "Look at us," she exclaimed, rolling her head from side to side. "Look how thin we got! Seventy times a day I climbed the stairs when father was in bed! Everybody tells me how bad I look, that I must take care of myself. We don't even have a chance to go to the movies. I haven't been to New York for over a year."

"And I have a cinch of it, is that it?" my father put in pepperily. "Well, I wish I could change places with you, that's all I want to say."

"Come now," said my mother, addressing my father as if he were a petulant child, "you know you shouldn't talk like that. We're doing our best, you know that."

"Yes," said my father, his tone getting more caustic, "and what about that cranberry juice I'm supposed to drink every day?"

With this my mother and sister turned on him savagely. How could he talk that way, they wanted to know, when they had been working themselves to the bone nursing and tending him? They turned to me. I must try to understand, they explained, that it was difficult sometimes to get out of the house, even to go as far as the corner.

"Couldn't you use the phone?" I asked.

The phone had been disconnected long ago, they told me. Another of my mother's economies, it seemed.

"But supposing something happened during the night?" I ventured to say.

"That's just what I tell them," my father put in. "That was mother's idea, shutting off the phone. I never approved of it."

"The things you say!" said my mother, trying to silence him with a frowning grimace. She turned to me, as if I were the very seat of reason. "All the neighbors have phones," she said. "Why, they won't even let me pay for a call—but of course I do in some other way. And then there's Teves up at the corner. . . ."

"You mean the undertaker?" I said.

"Yes," said my father. "You see, when the weather permits I often take a stroll as far as the corner. If Teves is there he brings a camp chair out for me—and if I want to make a call why I use his phone. He never charges me for it. He's been very decent, I must say that." And then he went on to explain to me how nice it was to be able to sit up there at the corner and watch the promenade. There was more life there, he reflected almost wistfully. "You know, one gets sick of seeing the same faces all the time, isn't that so?"

"I hope you're not sick of us!" said my mother reproachfully.

"You know that's not what I mean," replied my father, obviously a little weary of this sort of exchange.

As I got up to change my seat I noticed a pile of old newspapers on the rocker. "What are you doing with those?" I asked.

"Don't touch them!" screamed my sister. "Those are for me!"

My father quickly explained that my sister had taken to reading the papers since my absence. "It's good for her," he said, "it takes her mind off things. She's a little slow, though . . . always about a month behind."

"I am not," said my sister tartly. "I'm only two weeks behind. If we didn't have so much work to do I'd be up to date. The minister says. . . ."

"All right, you win," said my father, trying to shut her up. "You can't say a word in this house without stepping on some one's toes."

There was a Vox-Pox program due over the radio any minute. They wanted to know if I had ever heard it, but before I could say yes or no my sister put in her oar—she wanted to listen to the choir singing carols. "Perhaps he'd like to hear some more war news," said my mother. She said it as though, having just come from Europe, I had a special proprietary interest in the grand carnage.

"Have you ever heard Raymond Gram Swing?" asked my father.

I was about to tell him I hadn't when my sister informed us that he wasn't on this evening.

"How about Gabriel Heatter then?" said my father.

"He's no good," said my sister, "he's a Jew."

"What's that got to do with it?" said my father.

"I like Kaltenborn," said my sister. "He has such a beautiful voice."

"Personally," said my father, "I prefer Raymond Swing. He's very impartial. He always begins—'Good *Evening!*' Never 'Ladies and gentlemen' or 'My friends,' as President Roosevelt says. You'll see. . . ."

This conversation was like a victrola record out of the past. Suddenly the whole American scene, as it is portrayed over the radio, came flooding back—chewing gum, furniture polish, can openers, mineral waters, laxatives, ointments, corn cures, liver pills, insurance policies; the crooners with their eunuch-like voices; the comedians with their stale jokes; the puzzlers with their inane questions (how many matches in a cord of wood?); the Ford Sunday evening hour, the Bulova watch business, the xylophones, the quartets, the bugle calls, the roosters crowing, the canaries warbling, the chimes bringing tears, the songs of yesterday, the news fresh from the griddle, the facts, the facts, the facts. . . . Here it was again, the same old stuff, and as I was soon to discover, more stupefying and stultifying than ever. A man named Fadiman, whom I was later to see in the movies with a quartet of well informed nit-wits, had organized some kind of puzzle committee—*Information Please,* I think it was called. This apparently was the *coup de grâce* of the evening's entertainment and befuddlement. This was real education, so they informed me. I squirmed in my seat and tried to assume an air of genuine interest.

It was a relief when they shut the bloody thing off and settled down to telling me about their friends and neighbors, about the accidents and illnesses of which seemingly there was no end. Surely I remembered Mrs. Froehlich? Well, all of a sudden—she was the picture of health, mind you!—she was taken to the hospital to be operated on. Cancer of the bladder it was. Lasted only two months. And just before she died—"she doesn't know it," said my father, absent mindedly using the present tense—her husband met with an accident. Ran into a tree and had his head taken off—just as clean as a razor. The undertakers had sewn it back on, of course—wonderful job they made of it too. Nobody would have been able to tell it, seeing him lying there in the coffin. Marvelous what they can do nowadays, the old man reflected aloud. Anyway, that's how it was with Mrs. Froehlich. Nobody would have thought that those two would pass on so quickly. They were only in their fifties. . . .

Listening to their recital I got the impression that the whole neighborhood was crippled and riddled with malignant diseases. Everybody with whom they had any dealings, friend, relative, neighbor, butcher, letter-carrier, gas inspector, every one without exception carried about with him perpetually a little flower which grew out of his own body and which was named after one or the other of the familiar maladies, such as rheumatism, arthritis, pneumonia, cancer, dropsy, anemia, dysentery, meningitis, epilepsy, hernia, encephalitis, megalomania, chilblains, dyspepsia and so on and so forth. Those who weren't crippled, diseased or insane were out of work and living on relief. Those who could use their legs were on line at the movies waiting for the doors to be thrown open. I was reminded in a mild way of *Voyage au Bout de la Nuit*. The difference between these two worlds otherwise so similar lay in the standard of living; even those on relief were living under conditions which would have seemed luxurious to that suburban working class whom Céline writes about. In Brooklyn, so it seemed to me, they were dying of malnutrition of the soul. They lived on as vegetable tissue, flabby, sleep-drugged, disease-ridden carcasses with just enough intelligence to enable them to buy oil burners, radios, automobiles, newspapers, tickets for the cinema. One whom I had know as a ball-player when I was a boy was now a retired policeman who spent his evenings writing in old Gothic. He had composed the Lord's Prayer in this script on a small piece of cardboard, so they were telling me, and when it was finished he discovered that he had omitted a word. So he was doing it over again, had been at it over a month already. He lived with his sister, an old maid, in a lugubrious big house which they had inherited from their parents. They didn't want any tenants—it was too much bother. They never went anywhere, never visited anybody, never had any company. The sister was a gossip who sometimes took three hours to get from the house to the corner drug store. It was said that they would leave their money to the Old Folks' Home when they died.

My father seemed to know every one for blocks around. He also knew who came home late at night because, sitting in the parlor at the front window all hours of the night waiting for the water to flow, he got a slant on things such as he'd never had before. What amazed him apparently was the number of young women who came home alone at all hours of the night, some of them tight as a pig-skin. People no longer had to get up early to go to work, at least not in this neighborhood. When he was a boy, he remarked, work began at daylight and lasted till ten in the evening. At eight-thirty, while these good for nothings were still turning over in bed, he was already having a second breakfast, meaning some pumpernickel sandwiches and a pitcher of beer.

The recital was interrupted because the bag was beginning to fill up. In the kitchen my father emptied the contents of the bag into an old beer pitcher, examined it to see if the urine looked cloudy or sandy, and then emptied it in the toilet. His whole attention, since the advent of the bag, was concentrated on the quality and flow of his urine. "People say hello, how are you getting on, and then biffo! they forget about you," he said, as he came back and resumed his place by the window. It was a random remark, apropos of nothing as far as I can remember, but what he meant evidently was that others *could* forget whereas he couldn't. At night, on going to bed, he had always the comforting thought that in an hour or two he would be obliged to get up and catch the urine before it began to leak out of the hole which the doctor had drilled in his stomach. There were rags lying about everywhere, ready to catch the overflow, and newspapers, in order to prevent the bedding and furniture from being ruined by the endless flow. Sometimes it would take hours for the urine to begin flowing and at other times the bag would have to be emptied two or three times in quick succession; now and then it would come out in the natural way also, as well as from the tube and the wound itself. It was a humiliating sort of malady as well as a painful one.

Out of a clear sky my mother, in an obviously false natural voice, suddenly requested me to accompany her upstairs, saying that she wanted to show me some of the improvements which had been made during my absence. We no sooner got to the landing than she began explaining to me in muffled tones that my father's condition was incurable. "He'll never get well," she said, "it's . . . ," and she mentioned that word which has come to be synonymous with modern civilization, the word which holds the same terror for the man of to-day as did leprosy for the men of old. It was no surprise to me, I must say. If anything, I was amazed that it was only that and nothing more. What bothered me more than anything was the loud voice in which she was whispering to me, for the doors were all open and my father could easily have heard what she was saying had he tried. I made her walk me through the rooms and tell me in a natural voice about the various renovations, about the thermostat, for instance, which was hanging on the wall under my grandfather's portrait. That fortunately brought up the subject of the new oil burner, thus precipitating a hurried visit of inspection to the cellar.

The appearance of the cellar was a complete surprise. It had been denuded, the coal bins removed, the shelves taken out, the walls whitewashed. Like some mediaeval object used by alchemists, there stood the oil burner neat, immaculate, silent except for a spasmodic ticking whose rhythm was unpredictable. From the reverence with which my mother spoke of it I gathered that the oil burner was quite the most important object in the house. I gazed at it in fascination and astonishment. No more coal or wood, no ashes to haul, no coal gas, no watching, no fussing, no fuming, no dirt, no smoke; temperature always the same, one for day and one for night; the little instrument on the parlor wall regulated its functioning automatically. It was as though a magician had secreted himself in the walls of the house, a new electro-dynamic, super-heterodyne god of the hearth. The cellar, which had once been a frightening place filled with unknown treasures, had now become bright and habitable; one could serve lunch down there on the concrete floor. With the installation of the oil burner a good part of my boyhood was wiped out. Above all I missed the shelves where the wine bottles covered with cobwebs had been kept. There was no more wine, no more champagne, not even a case of beer. Nothing but the oil burner —and that peculiar, unnaturally rhythmed ticking which however muffled always gave me a start.

As we climbed the stairs I observed another sacred object also ticking in a mechanically epileptic way—the refrigerator. I hadn't seen a refrigerator since I left America and of course those I had known then were long since outmoded. In France I hadn't even used an ice-box, such as

ve had been accustomed to at home. I bought only as much
s was required for the current meal; what was perishable
perished, whatever turned sour turned sour, that was all.
Nobody I knew in Paris owned a refrigerator; nobody I
knew ever thought of refrigerators. As for Greece, where
coal was at a premium, the cooking was done on charcoal
stoves. And, if one had any culinary instincts, the meals
could be just as palatable, just as delicious and nourishing
as anywhere else. I was reminded of Greece and the charcoal stoves because I had suddenly become aware that the
old coal stove in the kitchen was missing, its place taken
now by a shining white enamelled gas range, another indis-
pensable, just-as-cheap and equally sacred object as the oil
burner and the refrigerator. I began to wonder if my mother
had become a little daffy during my absence. Was everybody installing these new conveniences? I inquired casually.
Most everybody, was the answer, including some who
couldn't afford to do so. The Gothic maniac and his sister
hadn't, to be sure, but then they were eccentric—they never
bought anything unless they had to. My mother, I couldn't
deny, had the good excuse that they were getting old and
that these little innovations meant a great saving of labor. I
was glad, in fact, that they had been able to provide for
themselves so well. At the same time, however, I couldn't
help but think of the old ones in Europe; they had not only
managed to do without these comforts but, so it seemed to
me, they remained far healthier, saner and more joyous
than the old ones in America. America has comforts; Europe has other things which make all these comforts seem
quite unimportant.

During the conversation which ensued my father brought
up the subject of the tailor shop which he hadn't set foot in
for over three years. He complained that he never heard a
word from his former partner. "He's too miserly to spend a
nickel on a telephone call," he said. "I know there was an
order from So-and-So for a couple of suits; that was about
six months ago. I haven't heard a word about it since." I
naturally volunteered to pay a visit to the shop one day and
inquire about things. "Of course," he said, *"he* doesn't have
to worry anymore whether things go or not. His daughter is
a movie star now, you know." It was possible too, he went

on to say, that the client had gone off on a cruise; he was always knocking about somewhere in his yacht. "By the time he comes in again he'll have either gained a few pounds or lost a few, and then everything will have to be altered. It may be a year or two before he's ready to take the clothes."

I learned that there were now about a dozen customers left on the books. No new ones forthcoming, of course. It was like the passing of the buffaloes. The man with the yacht who had ordered two precious suits of clothes, for which he was in no apparent hurry, used formerly to order a dozen at a time, to say nothing of cutaways, overcoats, dinner jackets, and so on. Nearly all the great merchant tailors of the past were either out of business, in bankruptcy, or about to give up. The great English woollen houses which had once served them were now shrunk to insignificant size. Though we have more millionaires than ever, fewer men seem inclined to pay $200.00 for an ordinary sack suit. Curious, what!

It was not only pathetic, it was ludicrous, to hear him talking about those two suits which, by the way, I was to remember to ask his partner not to leave hanging on the rack by the front window because they would be faded by the time the man called for a fitting. They had become mythical, legendary—the two suits ordered by a millionaire in the year '37 or '38 just prior to a short cruise in the Mediterranean. If all went well why possibly two years hence there would be ten or fifteen dollars accruing to the old man as his share of the transaction. Wonderful state of affairs! Somehow the two legendary suits belonged with the oil burner and the frigidaire—part and parcel of the same system of luxurious necessity and generous waste. Meantime, just to take a random shot, the fumes from the copper smelting plant at Ducktown, Tennessee, had rendered absolutely death-like and desolate the whole region for fifty miles around. (To see this region is to have a premonition of the fate of still another planet—our Earth—should the human experiment fail. Here Nature resembles the raw backside of a sick chimpanzee.) The president of the plant, undisturbed by the devastation, to say nothing of the premature deaths in the mines, may possibly be getting ready to order a hunting jacket on his coming trip to New York.

Or he may have a son who is preparing to enter the army as a brigadier-general for whom he will put in an order for the appropriate outfit when the time comes. That disease which boss tailors acquire, just like other people, won't be such a terrifying thing to the president of Copper Hill, should it strike him down, because with trained nurses to irrigate him every few hours and a specialist to summon by taxi when he has a little pain, he can have quite a tolerable time of it—perhaps not as much rich food as he is used to having, but plenty of good things just the same, including a game of cards every night or a visit to the cinema in his wheel chair.

As for my father, he has his little pleasure too every month or so, when he is given a joy ride to the doctor's office. I was a little annoyed that my father should be so grateful to his friend for acting as a chauffeur once a month. And when my mother began to lay it on about the kindness of the neighbors—letting her telephone free of charge and that sort of thing—I was about ready to explode. "What the devil," I remarked, "it's no great favor they're doing. A nigger would do as much for you—more maybe. That's the least one can do for a friend."

My mother looked aggrieved. She begged me not to talk that way. And in the next breath she went on to say how good the people next door were to her, how they left the morning paper for them at the window every evening. And another neighbor down the block was thoughtful enough to save the old rags which accumulated. Real Christians, I must say. Generous souls, what!

"And the Helsingers?" I said, referring to their old friends who were now millionaires. "Don't they do anything for you?"

"Well," my father began, "you know what a stinker he always was. . . ."

"How can you talk that way!" exclaimed my mother.

"I'm only telling the truth," said the old man innocently.

They had been very kind and thoughtful too, my mother tried to say. The proof of it was that they had remembered on their last visit—eight months ago—to bring a jar of preserves from their country estate.

"So that's it!" I broke out, always enraged by the very

mention of their name. "So that's the best they can do, is it?"

"They have their own troubles," said my mother reprovingly. "You know Mr. Helsinger is going blind."

"Good," I said bitterly. "I hope he grows deaf and dumb too—and paralyzed to boot."

Even my father thought this a bit too vehement. "Still," he said, "I can't say that I ever knew him to do a generous deed. He was always close, even from the beginning. But he's losing it all now—the boy is going through it fast."

"That's fine," I said. "I hope he loses every penny of it before he croaks. I hope he dies in want—and in pain and agony."

Here my sister suddenly popped up. "You shouldn't talk that way," she said, "you'll be punished for it. Pastor Liederkranz says we must only speak good of one another." And with the mention of the pastor's name she began to ramble on about Greece which his holiness, the Episcopal cheese of the diocese, had visited last year during his vacation.

"And what have they done for you all?" (meaning the church) I asked, turning to my father and mother.

"We never belonged to any church, you know," said my mother softly.

"Well, *she* belongs, doesn't she?" I said, nodding in my sister's direction. "Isn't that enough for them?"

"They have their own to take care of."

"Their own!" I said sneeringly. "That's a good excuse."

"He's right," said my father. "They could have done *something*. You take the Lutheran Church—we're not members of that either, but they send us things just the same, don't they. And they come and visit us, too. How do you explain that?" and he turned on my mother rather savagely, as if to show that he was a bit fed up with her continuous whitewashing of this one and that.

At this juncture my sister, who always became alert when the church was involved, reminded us that a new parish house was being built—there would be new pews installed too, we shouldn't forget that either. "That costs something!" she snarled.

"All right, you win!" yelled my father. I had to laugh. I had never realized before what an obstinate, tenacious creature my sister could be. Half-witted though she was, she seemed to realize that she needn't let my father bulldoze her any longer. She could even be cruel, in her witless way. "No, I won't get any cigarettes for you," she would say to the old man. "You smoke too much. We don't smoke and we're not sick."

The great problem, the old man confided to me when we were alone for a few minutes, was to be able to have a quarter in his pocket at all times—"in case anything should happen," as he put it. "They mean well," he said, "but they don't understand. They think I ought to cut out the cigarettes, for instance. By God, I have to do something to while away the time, don't I? Of course it means fifteen cents a day, but. . . ."

I begged him not to say any more about it. "I'll see that you have cigarettes at least," I said, and with that I fished out a couple of dollars and blushingly thrust the money in his hand.

"Are you sure you can spare it?" said my father, quickly hiding it away. He leaned forward and whispered: "Better not let them know you gave me anything—they'll take it away from me. They say I don't need any money."

I felt wretched and exasperated.

"Understand," he went on, "I don't mean to complain. But it's like the doctor business. Mother wants me to delay the visits as long as possible. It's not right, you know. If I wait too long the pains get unbearable. When I tell her that she says—'*it's your condition.*' Half the time I don't dare tell her I'm in pain; I don't want to annoy her. But I do think if I went a little oftener it would ease things up a bit, don't you?"

I was so choked with rage and mortification I could scarcely answer him. It seemed to me that he was being slowly tortured and humiliated; they behaved as if he had committed a crime by becoming ill. Worse, it was as if my mother, knowing that he would never get well, looked upon each day that he remained alive as so much unnecessary expense. She delighted in depriving herself of things, in order to impress my father with the need of economizing. Actually the only economy he could practise would be to die. That's how it looked to me, though I dare say if I had put it to my mother that way she would have been horrified. She was working herself to the bone, no doubt about that. And she had my sister working the treadmill too. But it was all stupid—unnecessary labor for the most part. They *created* work for themselves. When any one remarked how pale and haggard they looked they would reply with alacrity—"Well, some one has to keep going. We can't all afford to be ill." As though to imply that being ill was a sinful luxury.

As I say, there was a blend of stupidity, criminality and hypocrisy in the atmosphere. By the time I was ready to take leave my throat was sore from repressing my emotions. The climax came when, just as I was about to slip into my overcoat, my mother in a tearful voice came rushing up to me and, holding me by the arm, said: "Oh Henry, there's a thread on your coat!" A thread, by Jesus! That was the sort of thing she would give attention to! The way she uttered the word thread was as if she had spied a leprous hand sticking out of my coat pocket. All her tenderness came out in removing that little white thread from my sleeve. Incredible—and disgusting! I embraced them in turn rapidly and fled out of the house. In the street I allowed the tears to flow freely. I sobbed and wept unrestrainedly all the way to the elevated station. As I entered the train, as we passed the names of familiar stations, all of them recalling some old wound or humiliation, I began enacting in my mind the scene I had just been through, began describing it as if I were seated before the typewriter with a fresh piece of paper in the roller. "Jesus, don't forget that about the head that was sewn on," I would say to myself, the tears streaming down my face and blinding me. *"Don't forget this . . . don't forget that."* I was conscious that everybody's eyes were focused on me, but still I continued to weep and to write. When I got to bed the sobbing broke out again. I must have gone on sobbing in my sleep for in the early morning I heard someone rapping on the wall and awoke to find my face wet with tears. The outburst continued intermittently for about thirty-six hours; any little thing served to make me break out afresh. It was a complete purge which left me exhausted and refreshed at the same time.

On going for my mail the next day, as if in answer to my prayers, I found a letter from a man whom I thought was my enemy. It was a brief note saying that he had heard I was back and would I stop in to see him some time. I went at once and to my astonishment was greeted like an old friend. We had hardly exchanged greetings when he said to me: "I want to help you—what can I do for you?" These words, which were wholly unexpected, brought on another weeping fit. Here was a Jew whom I had met only once before, with whom I had exchanged barely a half dozen letters while in Paris, whom I had offended mortally by what he considered my anti-Semitic writings, and now suddenly, without a word of explanation for his *volte face,* he puts himself completely at my service. *I want to help you!* These words which one so seldom hears, especially when one is in distress, were not new to me. Time and again it has been my fortune to be rescued either by an enemy or by an utter stranger. It has happened so often, in fact, that I have almost come to believe that Providence is watching over me.

To be brief, I now had a sufficient sum in my pocket for my needs and the assurance that more was forthcoming should I need it. I passed from the anguish of utter doubt and despair to radiant, boundless optimism. I could return to the house of sorrow and bring a ray of cheer.

I telephoned immediately to communicate the good news. I told them I had found an editor for my work and had been given a substantial advance. I hinted that I would be shortly given a contract for a new book, a lie which was soon to become a fact. They were amazed and a bit sceptical, as they had always been. My mother, in fact, as though failing to grasp what I had said, informed me over the telephone that they could give me a little work to do, if I wanted it, such as painting the kitchen and repairing the roof. It would give me a little pocket money anyway, she added.

As I hung up the receiver it came back to me in a flash how long ago, when I had just begun to write, I used to sit at the window by the sewing table, and batter my brains trying to write the stories and essays which the editors never found acceptable. I remember the period well because it was one of the bitterest I have ever gone through. Because of our abject poverty my wife and I had decided to separate for a while. She had returned to her parents (so I thought!) and I was returning to mine. I had to swallow my pride and beg to be taken back to the fold. Of course there had never been any thought in their mind of refusing my request, but when they discovered that I had no intention of looking for a job, that I was still dreaming of earning a living by writing, their disappointment was soon converted into a deep chagrin. Having nothing else to do but eat, sleep and write I was up early every morning seated at the sewing table which my aunt had left behind when she was taken to the insane asylum. I worked until a neighbor called. The moment the bell rang my mother would come running to me and beg me frantically to put my things away, and hide myself in the clothes closet. She was ashamed to let any one know that I was wasting my time at such a foolish pursuit. More, she was even concerned for fear that I might be slightly touched. Consequently, as soon as I saw some one entering the gate I gathered up my paraphernalia, rushed with it to the bathroom, where I hid it in the tub, and then secreted myself in the clothes closet where I would stand in the dark choking with the stink of camphor balls until the neighbor took leave. Small wonder that I always associated my activity with that of the criminal! Often in my dreams I am taken to the penitentiary where I immediately proceed to install myself as comfortably as possible with typewriter and paper. Even when awake I sometimes fall into a reverie wherein, accommodating myself to the thought of a year or two behind the bars, I begin planning the book I will write during my incarceration. Usually I am provided with the sewing table by the window, the one on which the telephone stood; it is a beautiful inlaid table whose pattern is engraved in my memory. In the center of it is a minute spot to which my eyes were riveted when, during the period I speak of, I received one evening a telephone call from my wife saying that she was about to jump in the river. In the midst of a despair which had become so tremendous as to freeze all emotion I suddenly heard her tearful voice announcing that she could stand it no longer. She was calling to say goodbye—a brief, hysterical speech and then click! and she had vanished and her address was the river. Terrible as I felt I nevertheless had to conceal my feelings. To their query as to who had called I replied—"Oh, just a friend!" and I sat there for a moment or two gazing at the minute spot which had become the infinitesimal speck in the river where the body of my wife was slowly disappearing. Finally I roused myself, put on my hat and coat, and announced that I was going for a walk.

When I got outdoors I could scarcely drag my feet along. I thought my heart had stopped beating. The emotion I had experienced on hearing her voice had disappeared; I had become a piece of slag, a tiny hunk of cosmic debris void of hope, desire, or even fear. Knowing not what to do or where to turn I walked about aimlessly in that frozen blight which has made Brooklyn the place of horror which it is. The houses were still, motionless, breathing gently as people breathe when they sleep the sleep of the just. I walked blindly onward until I found myself on the border of the old neighborhood which I love so well. Here suddenly the significance of the message which my wife had transmitted over the telephone struck me with a new impact. Suddenly I grew quite frantic and, as if that would help matters, I instinctively quickened my pace. As I did so the whole of my life, from earliest boyhood on, began to unroll itself in swift and kaleidoscopic fashion. The myriad events which had combined to shape my life became so fascinating to me that, without realizing why or what, I found myself growing enthusiastic. To my astonishment I caught myself laughing and weeping, shaking my head from side to side, gesticulating, mumbling, lurching like a drunkard. I was alive again, that's what it was. I was a living entity, a human being capable of registering joy and sorrow, hope and despair. It was marvellous to be alive—just that and nothing more. Marvellous to have lived, to remember so much. If she had really jumped in the river then there was nothing to be done about it. Just the same I began to wonder if I oughtn't to go to the police and inform them about it. Even as the thought came to mind I espied a cop standing on the corner, and impulsively I started towards him. But when I came close and saw the expression on his face the impulse died as quickly as it had come. I went up to him nevertheless and in a calm, matter of fact tone I asked him he could direct me to a certain street, a street I knew well since it was the one I was living on. I listened to his directions as would a penitent prisoner were he to ask the way back to the penitentiary from which he had escaped.

When I got back to the house I was informed that my wife had just telephoned. "What did she say?" I exclaimed, almost beside myself with joy.

"She said she would call you again in the morning," said my mother, surprised that I should seem so agitated.

When I got to bed I began to laugh; I laughed so hard the bed shook. I heard my father coming upstairs. I tried to suppress my laughter but couldn't.

"What's the matter with you?" he asked, standing outside the bedroom door.

"I'm laughing," I said. "I just thought of something funny."

"Are you sure you're all right?" he said, his voice betraying his perplexity. "We thought you were crying. . . ."

I am on my way to the house with a pocketful of money. Unusual event for me, to say the least. I begin to think of the holidays and birthdays in the past when I arrived empty handed, sullen, dejected, humiliated and defeated. It embarrassing, after having ignored their circumstances all these years, to come trotting in with a handful of dough and say, "Take it, I know you need it!" It was theatrical, for one thing, and it was creating an illusion which might have to be sadly punctured. I was of course prepared for the ceremony my mother would go through. I dreaded that. It would have been easier to hand it to my father, but he would only be obliged to turn it over to my mother and that would creat more confusion and embarrassment.

"You shouldn't have done it!" said my mother, just as I had anticipated. She stood there holding the money in her hand and making a gesture as if to return it, as if she couldn't accept it. For a moment I had the uncomfortable feeling that she might possibly have thought I stole the money. It was not beyond me to do a thing like that, especially in such a desperate situation. However, it was not that, it was just that my mother had the habit, whenever she was offered a gift, be it a bunch of flowers, a crystal bowl or a discarded wrapper, of pretending that it was too much, that she wasn't worthy of such a kindness. "You oughtn't to have done it!" she would always say, a remark that always drove me crazy. "Why shouldn't people do things for one another?" I used to ask. "Don't you enjoy giving gifts yourself? Why do you talk that way?" Now she was saying to me, in that same disgusting fashion, "We know you can't afford it—why did you do it?"

"But didn't I tell you I *earned* it—and that I'll get lots more? What are you worrying about?"

"Yes," she said, blushing with confusion and looking as if I were trying to injure her rather than aid her, "but are you sure? Maybe they won't take your work after all. Maybe you'll have to return the money. . . ."

"For God's sake, stop it!" said my father. "Take it and be done with it! We can use it, you know that. You belly-ache when we have no money and you bellyache when you get it." He turned to me. "Good for you, son," he said. "I'm glad to see you're getting on. It's certainly coming to you."

I always liked my father's attitude about money. It was clean and honest. When he had he gave, until the last cent, and when he didn't have he borrowed, if he could. Like myself he had no compunctions about asking for help when he needed it. He took it for granted that people should help, because he himself was always the first to help when any one was in need. It's true he was a bad financier, it's true he made a mess of things. But I'm glad he was that way; it wouldn't seem natural to think of him as a million-aire. Of course, by not managing his affairs well he forced my mother to become the financier. Had she not contrived to salt a little away during the good years no doubt the three of them would have been in the poor house long ago. How much she had salvaged from the wreckage none of us knew, not even my father. Certainly, to observe the way she econ-omized, one would imagine it to be a very insignificant sum. Not a scrap of food ever went into the garbage can; no piece of string, no wrapping paper was ever thrown out; even the newspapers were preserved and sold at so much the pound.

The sweater which she wore when it got chilly was in rags. Not that she had no other, oh no! She was saving the others carefully—they were put away in camphor balls—until the day that the old one literally fell apart. The drawers, as I accidentally discovered when searching for something, were crammed full of things which would come in handy some time, some time when things would be much worse than now. In France I was accustomed to seeing this stupid conservation of clothes, furniture and other objects, but to see it happening in America, in our own home, was something of a shock. None of my friends had ever shown a sense of economy, nor any sentiment for old things. It wasn't the American way of looking at life. The American way has always been to plunder and exploit and then move on.

Now that the ice had been broken my visits to the house became quite frequent. It's curious how simple things are when they're faced. To think that for years I had dreaded the very thought of walking into that house, had hoped to die first and so on. Why, it was actually pleasant, I began to realize, to run back and forth, particularly when I could come with hands full as I usually did. It was so easy to make them happy—I almost began to wish for more difficult circumstances, in order to prove to them that I was equal to any emergency. The mere fact of my presence seemed to fortify them against all the hazards and dangers which the future might hold in store. Instead of being burdened by their problems, I began to feel lightened. What they asked of me was nothing compared to what I had stupidly imagined. I wanted to do more, much more, than anything they could think of asking me to do. When I proposed to them one day that I would come over early each morning and irrigate my father's bladder—a job which I felt my mother was doing incompetently—they were almost frightened. And when I followed that up, since they wouldn't hear of such a thing, by proposing to hire a nurse I could see from the expression on their faces that they thought I was losing my head. Of course they had no idea how guilty I felt, or if they had they were tactful enough to conceal it. I was bursting to make some sacrifice for them, but they didn't want sacrifices; all that they ever wanted of me, I slowly began to comprehend, was myself.

Sometimes in the afternoons, while the sun was still warm, I would sit in the backyard with my father and chat about old times. They were always proud of the little garden which they kept there. As I walked about examining the shrubs and plants, the cherry tree and the peach tree which they had grown since I left, I recalled how as a boy I had planted each little bush. The lilac bushes in particular impressed me. I remembered the day they were given me, when I was on a visit to the country, and how the old woman had said to me—"They will probably outlast you, my young bucko." Nothing was dying here in the garden. It would be beautiful, I thought to myself, if we were all buried in the garden among the things we had planted and watched over so lovingly. There was a big elm tree a few yards away. I was always fond of that tree, fond of it because of the noise it made when the wind soughed through the thick foliage. The more I gazed at it now the more its personality grew on me. I almost felt as if I would be able to talk to that tree if I sat there long enough.

Other times we would sit in the front, in the little area-way where once the grass plot had been. This little realm was also full of memories, memories of the street, of summer nights, of mooning and pining and planning to break away. Memories of fights with the children next door who used to delight in tantalizing my sister by calling her crazy. Memories of girls passing and longing to put my arms around them. And now another generation was passing the door and they were regarding me as if I were an elderly gentleman. "Is that your brother I see sitting with you sometimes?" some one asked my father. Now and then an old playmate would pass and my father would nudge me and say—"There goes Dick So-and-So" or "Harry this or that." And I would look up and see a middle-aged man passing, a man I would never have recognized as the boy I once used to play with. One day it happened that as I was going to the corner a man came towards me, blocking my path, and as I tried to edge away he planked himself square in front of me and stood there gazing at me fixedly, staring right through me. I thought he was a detective and was not altogether sure whether he had made a mistake or not. "What do you want?" I said coldly, making as if to move on. *"What do I want?"* he echoed."What the hell, don't you recognize an old friend any more?" "I'm damned if I know who you are," I said. He stood there grinning and leering at me. "Well, I know who *you* are," he said. With that my memory came back. "Why of course," I said, "it's Bob Whalen. Of course I know you; I was just trying to kid you." But I would never have known him had he not forced me to remember. The incident gave me such a start then when I got back to the house I went immediately to the mirror and scrutinized my countenance, trying in vain to detect the changes which time had made in it. Not satisfied, and still inwardly disturbed, I asked to see an early photograph of myself. I looked at the photograph and then at the image in the mirror. There was no getting around it —it was not the same person. Then suddenly I felt apologetic for the casual way in which I had dismissed my old boyhood friend. Why, come to think of it, we had been just as close as brothers once. I had a strong desire to go out and telephone him, tell him I would be over to see him and have a good chat. But then I remembered that the reason why we had ceased relations, upon growing to manhood, was because he had become an awful bore. At twenty-one he had already become just like his father whom he used to hate as a boy. I couldn't understand such a thing then; I attributed it to sheer laziness. So what would be the good of suddenly renewing our friendship? I knew what his father was like; what good would it do to study the son? We had only one thing in common—our youth, which was gone. And so I dismissed him from my mind then and there. I buried him, as I had all the others from whom I had parted.

Sitting out front with my father the whole miniature world of the neighborhood passed in review. Through my father's comments I was privileged to get a picture of the life of these people such as would have been difficult to obtain otherwise. At first it seemed incredible to me that he should know so many people. Some of those whom he greeted lived blocks away. From the usual neighborly salutations relations had developed until they became genuine friendships. I looked upon my father as a lucky man. He was never lonely, never lacking visitors. A steady stream passed in and out of the house bringing thoughtful little gifts or words of encouragement. Clothes, foodstuffs, medicines, toilet articles, magazines, cigarettes, candy, flowers—everything but money poured in liberally. "What do you need money for?" I said one day. "Why, you're a rich man." "Yes," he said meekly, "I certainly can't complain."

"Would you like me to bring you some books to read?" I asked another time. "Aren't you tired of looking at the magazines?" I knew he never read books but I was curious to see what he would answer.

"I used to read," he said, "but I can't concentrate any more."

I was surprised to hear him admit that he had ever read a book. "What sort of books did you read?" I asked.

"I don't remember the titles any more," he said. "There was one fellow—Ruskin, I think it was."

"You read *Ruskin?*" I exclaimed, positively astounded.

"Yes, but he's pretty dry. That was a long time ago, too."

The conversation drifted to the subject of painting. He remembered with genuine pleasure the paintings with which his boss, an English tailor, had once decorated the walls of the shop. All the tailors had paintings on their walls then, so he said. That was back in the '80's and '90's. There must have been a great many painters in New York at that time, to judge from the stories he told me. I tried to find out what sort of paintings the tailors went in for at that period. The paintings were traded for clothes, of course.

He began to reminisce. There was So-and-so, he was saying. He did nothing but sheep. But they were wonderful sheep, so life-like, so real. Another man did cows, another dogs. He asked me parenthetically if I knew Rosa Bonheur's work—those wonderful horses! And George Inness! There was a great painter, he said enthusiastically. "Yes," he added meditatively, "I never got tired of looking at them. It's nice to have paintings around." He didn't think much of the modern painters—too much color and confusion, he thought. "Now Daubigny," he said, "there was a great painter. Fine sombre colors—something to think about." There was one large canvas, it seems, which he was particularly fond of. He couldn't remember any more who had painted it. Anyway, the thing which impressed him was that nobody would buy this painting, though it was acknowledged to be a masterpiece. "You see," he said, "it was too sad. People don't like sad things." I wondered what the subject could have been. "Well," he said, "it was a picture of an old sailor returning home. His clothes were falling off his back; he looked glum and melancholy. But it was wonderfully done—I mean the expression on his face. But nobody would have it; they said it was depressing."

As we were talking he paused to greet some one. I waited a few minutes until he beckoned me to approach and be introduced. "This is Mr. O'Rourke," he said, "he's an astrologer." I pricked up my ears. "An astrologer?" I echoed. Mr. O'Rourke modestly replied that he was just a student. "I don't know so very much about it," he said, "but I did tell your father that you would return and that things would change for the better with your coming. I knew that you must be an intelligent man—I studied your horoscope carefully. Your weakness is that you're too generous, you give right and left."

"Is that a weakness?" I said laughingly.

"You have a wonderful heart," he said, "and a great intelligence. You were born lucky. There are great things in store for you. I told your father that you will be a great man. You'll be very famous before you die."

My father had to run inside a moment to empty the bag. I stood chatting with Mr. O'Rourke a few minutes. "Of course," he said, "I must also tell you that I say a prayer every night for your father. That helps a great deal, you know. I try to help everybody—that is, if they will listen to me. Some people, of course, you can't help—they won't let you. I'm not very fortunate myself but I have the power to aid others. You see, I have a bad Saturn. But I try to overcome it with prayer—and with right living, of course. I was telling your mother the other day that she has five good years ahead of her. She was born under the special protection of St Anthony—June the 13th is her birthday, isn't it? St Anthony never turns a deaf ear to those who beseech his favor."

"What does he do for a living?" I asked my father when Mr. O'Rourke had gone.

"He doesn't do anything, as far as I can make out," said my father. "I think he's on relief. He's a queer one, isn't he? I was wondering if I shouldn't give him that old overcoat that mother put away in the trunk. I've got enough with this one. You notice he looks a bit seedy."

There were lots of queer ones walking about the street. Some had become religious through misfortune and sorrow. There was one old woman who sent my father Christian Science tracts. Her husband had become a drunkard and deserted her. Now and then she would drop in to see my father and explain the writings of the Master. "It's not all nonsense," said my father. "Everything has its points, I suppose. Anyway, they don't mean any harm. I listen to them all. Mother thinks it's silly, but when you have nothing to do it takes your mind off things."

It was strange to me to see how the church had finally gotten its grip on every one. It seemed to lie in wait for the opportune moment, like some beast of prey. The whole family seemed to be touched with one form of religiosity or another. At one of the family reunions I was shocked to see an old uncle suddenly rise and pronounce grace. Thirty years ago any one who had dared to make a gesture like that would have been ridiculed and made the butt of endless jokes. Now everybody solemnly bowed his head and listened piously. I couldn't get over it. One of my aunts was now a deaconess. She loved church work, especially during festivities, when there were sandwiches to be made. They spoke of her proudly as being capable of waiting on fifty people at once. She was clever, too, at wrapping up gifts. On one occasion she had astounded everybody by presenting some one with a huge umbrella box. And what do you suppose was in the umbrella box when they undid it? Five ten-dollar bills! Quite original! And that was the sort of thing she had learned at the church, through all the fairs and bazaars and what not. So you see. . . .

During one of these reunions a strange thing happened to me. We were celebrating somebody's anniversary in the old house which my grandfather had bought when he came to America. It was an occasion to meet all the relatives at once—some thirty to forty aunts, cousins, nephews, nieces. Once again, as in olden times, we would all sit down to table together, a huge creaking board laden with everything imaginable that was edible and potable. The prospect pleased me, particularly because of the opportunity it would give me to have another look at the old neighborhood.

While the gifts were being distributed—a ceremony which usually lasted several hours—I decided to sneak outdoors and make a rapid exploration of the precincts. Immediately I set foot outdoors I started instinctively in search of the little street about which I used to dream so frequently while in Paris. I had been on this particular street only two or three times in my life, as a boy of five or six. The dream, I soon discovered, was far more vivid than the actual scene. There were elements which were missing now, not so much because the neighborhood had changed but because these elements had never existed, except in my dreams. There were two realities which in walking through the street now began to fuse and form a composite living truth which, if I were to record faithfully, would live forever. But the most curious thing about this incident lies not in the fitting together of the dream street and the actual street but the discovery of a street I had never known, a street only a hand's throw away, which for some reason had escaped my attention as a child. This street, when I came upon it in the evening mist, had me gasping with joy and astonishment. Here was the street which corresponded exactly with that ideal street which, in my dream wanderings, I had vainly tried to find.

In the recurrent dream of the little street which I first mentioned the scene always faded at the moment when I came upon the bridge that crossed the little canal, neither the bridge nor the canal having any existence actually. This evening, after passing beyond the frontier of my childhood explorations, I suddenly came upon the very street I had been longing to find for so many years. There was in the atmosphere here something of another world, another planet. I remember distinctly the premonition I had of approaching this other world when, passing a certain house, I caught sight of a young girl, obviously of foreign descent, poring over a book at the dining room table. There is nothing unique, to be sure, in such a sight. Yet, the moment my eyes fell upon the girl I had a thrill beyond description,

a premonition, to be more accurate, that important revelations were to follow. It was as if the girl, her pose, the
glow of the room falling upon the book she was reading,
the impressive silence in which the whole neighborhood
was enveloped, combined to produce a moment of such
acuity that for an incalculably brief, almost meteoric flash I
had the deep and quiet conviction that everything had been
ordained, that there was justice in the world, and that the
image which I had caught and vainly tried to hold was the
expression of the splendor and the holiness of life as it
would always reveal itself to be in moments of utter still-
ness. I realized as I pushed ecstatically forward that the
joy and bliss we experience in the profound depths of the
dream—a joy and bliss which surpasses anything known
in waking life—comes indubitably from the miraculous
accord between desire and reality. When we come to the
surface again this fusion, this harmony, which is the whole
goal of life, either falls apart or else is only fitfully and
feebly realized. In our waking state we toss about in a troubled sleep, the sleep which is terrifying and death-dealing
because our eyes are open, permitting us to see the trap into
which we are walking and which we are nevertheless unable
to avoid.

The interval between the moment of passing the girl and
the first glimpse of the long-awaited ideal street, which I
had searched for in all my dreams and never found, was of
the same flavor and substance as those anticipatory moments in the deep dream when it seems as if no power on
earth can hinder the fulfillment of desire. The whole character of such dreams lies in the fact that once the road
has been taken the end is always certain. As I walked past
the row of tiny houses sunk deep in the earth I saw what
man is seldom given to see—the reality of his vision. To me
it was the most beautiful street in the world. Just one block
long, dimly lit, shunned by respectable citizens, ignored by
the whole United States—a tiny community of foreign souls
living apart from the great world, pursuing their own humble ways and asking nothing more of their neighbors than
tolerance. As I passed slowly from door to door I saw that
they were breaking bread. On each table there was a bottle
of wine, a loaf of bread, some cheese and olives and a bowl

of fruit. In each house it was the same: the shades were up, the lamp was lit, the table spread for a humble repast. And always the occupants were gathered in a circle, smiling good-naturedly as they conversed with one another, their bodies relaxed, their spirit open and expansive. Truly, I thought to myself, this is the only life I have ever desired. For the briefest intervals only have I known it and then it has been rudely shattered. And the cause? Myself undoubtedly, my inability to realize the true nature of Paradise. As a boy, knowing nothing of the great life outside this ambiance of the little world, the holy, cellular life of the microcosm, must have penetrated deep. What else can explain the tenacity with which I have clung for forty years to the remembrance of a certain neighborhood, a certain wholly inconspicuous spot on this great earth? When my feet began to itch, when I became restless in my own soul, I thought it was the larger world, the world outside, calling to me, beseeching me to find a bigger and greater place for myself. I expanded in all directions. I tried to embrace not only this world but the worlds beyond. Suddenly, just when I thought myself emancipated, I found myself thrust back into the little circle from which I had fled. I say "the little circle," meaning not only the old neighborhood, not only the city of my birth, but the whole United States. As I have explained elsewhere, Greece, tiny though it appears on the map, was the biggest world I have ever entered. Greece for me was the home which we all long to find. As a country it offered me everything I craved. And yet, at the behest of the American consul in Athens, I consented to return. I accepted the American consul's intervention as the bidding of fate. In doing so I perhaps converted what is called blind fate into something destined. Only the future will tell if this be so. At any rate, I came back to the narrow, circumscribed world from which I had escaped. And in coming back I not only found everything the same, but even more so. How often since my return have I thought of Nijinsky who was so thoughtlessly awakened from his trance! What must he think of this world on which he had deliberately turned his back in order to avoid becoming insane like the rest of us! Do you suppose he feels thankful to his specious benefactors? Will he stay awake and toss fitfully in his sleep, as we do, or will he choose to close his eyes again and feast only upon that which he knows to be true and beautiful?

The other day, in the office of a newspaper, I saw in big letters over the door: "Write the things which thou hast seen and the things which are." I was startled to see this exhortation, which I have religiously and unwittingly followed all my life, blazing from the walls of a great daily. I had forgotten that there were such words recorded in *Revelations. The things which are!* One could ponder over that phrase forever. One thing is certain, however, and that is that the things which are are eternal. I come back to that little community, that dream world, in which I was raised. In microcosm it is a picture of that macrocosm which we call the world. To me it is a world asleep, a world in which the dream is imprisoned. If for a moment there is an awakening the dream, vaguely recalled, is speedily forgotten. This trance, which continues twenty-four hours of the day, is only slightly disturbed by wars and revolutions. Life goes on, as we say, but smothered, damped down, hidden away in the vegetative fibres of our being. Real awareness comes intermittently, in brief flashes of a second's duration. The man who can hold it for a minute, relatively speaking, inevitably changes the whole trend of the world. In the span of ten or twenty thousand years a few widely isolated individuals have striven to break the deadlock, shatter the trance, as it were. Their efforts, if we look at the present state of the world superficially, seem to have been ineffectual. And yet the example which their lives affords us points conclusively to one thing, that the real drama of man on earth is concerned with Reality and not with the creation of civilizations which permit the great mass of men to snore more or less blissfully. A man who had the slightest awareness of what he was doing could not possibly put his finger to the trigger of a gun, much less cooperate in the making of such an instrument. A man who wanted to live would not waste even a fraction of a moment in the invention, creation and perpetuation of instruments of death. Men are more or less reconciled to the thought of death, but they also know that it is not necessary to kill one another. They know it intermittently, just as they know other things which they conveniently proceed to forget when there is danger of having their sleep disturbed. To live without killing is a thought which could electrify the world, if men were only capable of staying awake long enough to let the idea soak in. But man refuses to stay awake because if he did he would be obliged to become something other than he now is, and the thought of that is apparently too painful for him to endure. If man were to come to grips with his real nature, if he were to discover his real heritage, he would become so exalted, or else so frightened, that he would find it impossible to go to sleep again. To live would be a perpetual challenge to create. But the very thought of a possible swift and endless metamorphosis terrifies him. He sleeps now, not comfortably to be sure, but certainly more and more obstinately, in the womb of a creation whose only need of verification is his own awakening. In this state of sublime suspense time and space have become meaningless concepts. Already they have merged to form another concept which, in his stupor, he is as yet unable to formulate or elucidate. But whatever the role that man is to play in it, the universe, of that we may be certain, is not asleep. Should man refuse to accept his role there are other planets, other stars, other suns waiting to go forward with the experiment. No matter how vast, how total, the failure of man here on earth, the work of man will be resumed elsewhere. War leaders talk of resuming operations on this front and that, but man's front embraces the whole universe.

In our sleep we have discovered how to exterminate one another. To abandon this pleasant pursuit merely to sleep more soundly, more peacefully, would be of no value. We must awaken—or pass out of the picture. There is no alarm clock which man can invent to do the trick. To set the alarm is a joke. The clock itself is an evidence of wrong thinking. What does it matter what time you get up if it is only to walk in your sleep?

Now extinction seems like true bliss. The long trance has dulled us to everything which is alive and awake. Forward! cry the defenders of the great sleep. *Forward to death!* But on the last day the dead will be summoned from their graves; they will be made to take up the life eternal. To postpone the eternal is impossible. Everything else we may do or fail to do, but eternity has nothing to do with time, nor sleep, nor failure, nor death. Murder is postponement. And war is murder, whether it be glorified by the righteous or not. I speak of the things which are, not because they are of the moment but because they always have been and always will be. The life which every one dreams of, and which no one has the courage to lead, can have no existence in the present. The present is only a gateway between past and future. When we awaken we will dispense with the fiction of the bridge which never existed. We will pass from dream to reality with eyes wide open. We will get our bearings instantly, without the aid of instruments. We will not need to fly around the earth in order to find the paradise which is at our feet. When we stop killing—not only actually, but in our hearts—we will begin to live, and not until then.

I believe that it is now possible for me to have my being anywhere on earth. I regard the entire world as my home. I inhabit the earth, not a particular portion of it labelled America, France, Germany or Russia. I owe allegiance to mankind, not to a particular country, race or people. I answer to God and not to the Chief Executive, whoever he may happen to be. I am here on earth to work out my own private destiny. My destiny is linked with that of every other living creature inhabiting this planet—perhaps with those on other planets too, who knows? I refuse to jeopardize my destiny by regarding life within the narrow rules which are now laid down to circumscribe it. I dissent from the current view of things as regards murder, as regards religion, as regards society, as regards our well-being. I will try to live my life in accordance with the vision I have of things eternal. I say "Peace to you all!" and if you don't find it, it's because you haven't looked for it.

Other SIGNET Books You Will Enjoy

A DEVIL IN PARADISE　　　　　**by Henry Miller**

In this brilliant new book, the dynamic author of *Tropic of Cancer* tells the tense story of an eccentric visitor, a strange man who attempts to dominate everyone in his orbit.　　　　　(#S1317—35¢)

NIGHTS OF LOVE AND LAUGHTER　　**by Henry Miller**

This fascinating volume contains moving tales in a variety of American and European settings.　　(#S1246—35¢)

ON THE ROAD　　　　　**by Jack Kerouac**

The mad coast-to-coast odyssey of young people in search for the ultimate in sensation.　　(#D1619—50¢)

BREAD AND WINE　　　　　**by Ignazio Silone**

This compelling novel of Italy under fascism has humor, tragedy, compassion and wisdom.　　(#D1545—50¢)

ROMAN TALES　　　　　**by Alberto Moravia**

Stories of the exuberant life in the back streets and slums of Rome, by Italy's greatest living writer, author of *The Woman of Rome*.　　(#S1612—35¢)

THE SOUND AND THE FURY　　**by William Faulkner**

The Nobel Prize winner's famous story of a proud and doomed Southern family. Coming as a film starring Yul Brynner, Joanne Woodward, Margaret Leighton, Ethel Waters.　　(#D1628—50¢)

NINE STORIES　　　　　**by J. D. Salinger**

Nine perceptive stories about young people in search of love by one of America's most outstanding modern writers.　　(#D1667—50¢)

To Our Readers: We welcome your comments about any SIGNET, SIGNET KEY, or MENTOR Book. If your dealer does not have the books you want, you may order them by mail, enclosing the list price plus 5¢ a copy to cover mailing. Send for our free catalog. The New American Library of World Literature, Inc., 501 Madison Avenue, N. Y. 22, N. Y.